The

NATURAL SCIENCES KNOW NOTHING of EVOLUTION

by

A. E. Wilder-Smith

MASTER BOOKS
A Division of
CLP Publishers
San Diego, California

The Natural Sciences Know Nothing of Evolution

Translated from the original German by Petra Wilder-Smith.

© 1981 A. E. Wilder-Smith

Published by
MASTER BOOKS
A Division of CLP Publishers
P. O. Box 15666
San Diego, California 92115

ISBN 0-89051-062-8
Library of Congress Catalog Card No. 80-67425

Cataloging in Publication Data
Wilder-Smith, A. E.
  The natural sciences know nothing of evolution.
  1. Natural History. 2. Evolution.
I. Title.

500   80-67425
ISBN 0-89051-062-8

Printed in the United States of America

Table of Contents

Preface

On January 14, 1975, in Zurich, Nobel Prize laureate Jacques Monod stated that today no one any longer harbors doubts regarding evolution. Everybody admits that it took place.[1] If Monod thus wished to express the idea that every single form of life (plant, animal, human) developed ontogenetically from nonliving matter, then he may have been entirely correct. But if, as was probably the case, he meant that man shares common ancestors with all animals and plants—that is, that transformism, the changing of one species into another higher one, took place—then many highly qualified biologists will protest. For in the course of the last few years, a number of mostly young experts have become convinced that biogenesis, the origin of life, is to be understood polyphylogenetically (from many sources) rather than monophylogenetically (all life stemming from one primeval cell). So today well-informed experts exist who no longer believe that all species originated from one primeval cell by means of transformism. They believe in no common biological family tree for all species, possessing a single root for all forms of life. Rather, they hold the opinion that life resembles a field in which many organisms flourish side by side without necessarily being connected phylogenetically.

G. A. Kerkut, Professor of Physiology and Biochemistry, University of Southampton, England, is one of the Professors who has questioned the old Neodarwinian transformism. Professor Kerkut writes: "The attempt to explain all living forms in terms of an evolution from a

---

[1]Jacques Monod: "L'évolution Microscopique." Lecture (Zurich, Jan. 14, 1975. Tape recording.)

unique source, though a brave and valid attempt, is one that is premature and not satisfactorily supported by present-day evidence."[2]   Kerkut adds that, personally, he would never state that evolution "has been proven beyond all reasonable doubt." He admits finding depressing the dogmatism of evolutionary theorists in many scientific circles.

Kerkut is one of the scientists in the USA, Europe, and England who is "on the move" regarding evolutionary theory. They no longer accept the old biogenetical dogmas concerning evolution. They regard them in the light of new knowledge in the fields of information theory and molecular biology. Against this background they examine the old theories. Highly qualified academics and professors of reputable universities in the Anglo-Saxon world and in Europe today no longer believe in a transformism of the old Neodarwinian type, where a primeval cell is supposed to have changed into all the species of our present biology solely through the forces of chance and natural selection. Today it is clearly not objective to state that only ignorant people refute the Neodarwinian theories. To classify doubting academics as ignorant is an emotional matter. Such outbreaks of emotion occurred many years ago in the defense of the Phlogiston theory which was formerly accepted by nearly all "educated" persons.

From a practical point of view two methods exist for testing the theory of evolution:

1. Theoretical examination, with the aid of the known laws of nature in order to discover whether, theoretically, spontaneous biogenesis from nonliving molecules could be possible. Pasteur's work on spontaneous biogenesis which yielded solely negative results was, of course, of a practical nature. If an experiment is unsuccessful today, why should it have been successful in the past under the same

---

[2]G. A. Kerkut: *Implications of Evolution.* Pergamon Press (Oxford, 1965) p. VII, VIII.

experimental conditions? The properties of matter and energy have remained identical today with those of the past. Pasteur's work was purely experimental, which, of course, has certain advantages—it can be repeated as often as one likes. Such attempts have always given negative results.

But one can work purely theoretically, too, to determine whether spontaneous biogenesis could, in theory, be possible. In the ensuing chapters we shall tread theoretical and experimental paths. Pasteur's experiments have long since proven in practice that even under the most favorable conditions spontaneous biogenesis does not take place. Every canning factory proves the same thing daily, so that we do not wish to over-emphasize this already well-worn path again at this stage.

2. Biological organisms of a past age (in the form of fossils) and living organisms of the present age can be examined for traces of transformism. If transformism corresponds to the biological facts, geological formations should be full of biological transitional forms clearly confirming transformism. These are the missing links which are so conspicuous by their absence in the fossil world. Among experts even the evidence for ostensible transitional stages in the so-called evolution of the horse are today being strongly criticized.[3] These and other questions are considered more closely later in the text.

Martin Jost[4] compares the above two investigative methods with another type of problem. The object of this problem is to determine whether all the electric plugs in a certain skyscraper function. In principle, the person in

---

[3] cf Martin Jost: "Abkehr von der Evolutionstheorie," *Schweizerische Akademiker und Studentenzeitung.* No. 51 (Nov. 1976). cf Kerkut, G.A., *Implications of Evolution,* Pergamon Press (Oxford, 1965).

[4] Jost: *op cit* (Ann. 3) p. 5.

charge has a choice between only two methods of investigation:

a. He could go from room to room and test to see whether there really is electricity in every single room plug. Naturally this method would be time consuming. There exists here, of course, the possibility of small errors. Or

b. He goes into the cellar of the skyscraper, and there he tests whether the mains are carrying current. If he is convinced that the mains are "dead," he no longer needs to visit individually the various rooms in the skyscraper. For he is sure that they all must be "dead" too, since the mains are carrying no current.

Now if it is found with certainty, both experimentally and theoretically, that spontaneous biogenesis and spontaneous automatic transformism of one species into another *higher* one *does not* and indeed *cannot* take place, then it will no longer be necessary to examine the various small branches of the evolutionary family tree. If the "root" cannot function, the rest of the "tree" no longer needs to be examined.

In the following chapters we not only wish to thoroughly examine the root of the evolutionary tree for its ability to function, but simultaneously we shall also test various "plugs" in the various stages of the evolutionary system for "current." Yet before we turn to this central task, we should like to mention some basic theoretical problems, which crop up repeatedly—but which are seldom treated frankly.

The real problem in Neodarwinian evolutionary teaching lies in the following theoretical, seldom specifically formulated assumptions:

1. The origins of the coded programs in the biological cell are attributed to chance and the autoorganization of inorganic material. As shown later in this text, this supposition is categorically untenable according to the tenets of modern information theory.

2. Leading modern Neodarwinians attribute the development of new genetic information to molecular variations which are then "fixed" by "gene mechanisms."

From a theoretical point of view the lowering of entropy (or an increase of order) can certainly be brought about in this manner with the help of "machines." But then the Neodarwinians state that *this decreased entropy represents new genetic information.* Thus Eigen, for example, says that the development of genetic, coded information in the biological cell, that is, of new genetic information, represents simple lowering of entropy. With the aid of principles behind information theory, it is shown in the text that *a simple decrease in entropy is not equivalent to the arising of programmed new information.* This being the case, the Neodarwinian hypothesis offers *no explanation for the greatest phenomenon in life:* the development of the coded genetic information which makes life possible and which, from a purely biological point of view *is* life. Accordingly, Neodarwinian thought stands helplessly before the real problem of biogenesis and biology and can help us no further in the principles behind these matters. Consequently, clinging to Neodarwinian principles effectively blocks research in the area of biogenesis and prevents progress. It desperately, and as as a matter of principle, retains an erroneous idea of the genesis of information within the genetic code by chance.

3. Darwinian transformism demands spontaneously increasing genetic information. The information on the chromosomes of the primitive cell must become greater for the primeval cell to become a human one. Just as mere molecular movements are incapable of producing information *de novo* (they can modify already existing information), neither can they produce *new* information, as will be shown in the text later. Neodarwinian theory does not enlighten us as to how a primeval cell can energetically finance the production of new information, so that it becomes a higher plant or a higher animal cell. Transformism demands a very large increase in information, the principle behind which Neodarwinian thought is incapable of explaining.

4. From a purely biochemical aspect, the cell consists of many chemical and physiological mechanisms of various types. These mechanisms may be generally defined as teleonomic machines or systems. Of course machines and mechanisms exhibit systems and aims unknown to raw inorganic matter. How can matter organize itself into a machine, if matter itself knows of no system (the very basis of all machines)? It is precisely at this point that Neodarwinism collides head-on with the second law of thermodynamics, which lays down the principle that matter, on its own, does not organize itself to higher order. In a closed system entropy and disorder increase, which is not quite congruent with the statement that raw matter builds machines and mechanisms—it does not—not even if "raw" energy is supplied and the system thus "opened." We have treated this problem in detail in the text. As regards the so-called autoorganization of matter, Neodarwinism is without either a theoretical or an experimental basis.

5. Let us consider the following proposition: An engineer from the outer galaxies visits the earth with some of his colleagues—after all life here has been extinguished by a nuclear war. Under the rubble he finds several cars which still function, finds their owners' manuals (in English), drives them, takes them apart, teaches himself metallurgy and mechanics from them, and finally builds a similar car from scrap metal and plastic leftovers. When other colleagues from the outer galaxies visit him, they ask him about the genesis of the first car. He replies that he is now completely familiar with all the natural laws governing the cars and is convinced that nothing but matter and the natural laws are behind autogenesis. Merely matter and the laws of nature were at work in constructing the car he found in the first place. By this reasoning, the laws of nature alone built the first car from matter.

In reality of course, the cars function *within* the laws of nature and of matter, just as the biological cell—also a machine—functions within the laws of nature and matter. Yet the laws of nature alone built neither the car nor the cell. For these laws are not teleonomic and therefore *build* no teleonomic machines. Darwinism has completely overlooked this important point—that the laws of nature do in fact provide the basis for the *functioning* of a machine, without at the same time being responsible for its *genesis*.

6. Evolution and transformism require the existence today of transitional stages between the species, both as living animals and also within the geological layers as fossils; however, neither are to be found in the present nor in the past. This fact is very comprehensible, for intermediate stages, e.g. stages between whales and land mammals, would have great difficulty in surviving. Physiologically such can hardly be envisioned. In geological formations transitional forms do not exist—neither among whales and land mammals, nor even among horses!

As a theoretical concept Neodarwinism proves to be chemically, physiologically, and physically untenable. A false concept will only serve to lead scientific research concepts astray. Since the discovery of the genetic code as the basis of biology, we urgently need a program of abiogenetical research which takes into account the genesis of codes, information, and of programs. However, this need will never be met if chance (noncode) is considered to be the basis of program information and code. Since Darwin, biological research has stood under the ban of the concept of chance and selection as the basic cause behind information, codes, and programs.

Today we live in an age of information and programming. These provide the technical basis both of the genetic code and of modern technology. For such an age, chance and selection no longer suffice—either as a philosophy for abiogenesis or for life itself. In the domain of technology and biology, chance no longer suffices as the basis of codes and programs, and yet chance is the very basis of all Neodarwinian abiogenetical thought. We most urgently need a complementing of our biology by the concepts of teleonomy and programming which are diametrically opposed to those of chance. Teleonomy and programming are the very antipodes of chance and aimless variations (which today are ostensibly still supposed to be the basis of genetic information in biology). Antipodes lie 180° apart. Thus Darwinian abiogenetical thought will need to rotate through 180° to be capable of catching up on progress in other areas of information theory and general science.

Chapter 1
Evolution As a Scientific Pseudofact

The Meaning of "Evolution"

Before we approach the actual problem of whether or not evolution is scientific, we need to define our terminology. By science, of course, we are referring to experimental science; that is, to those sciences which deal with definite, experimental, regularly repeatable results and not merely philosophy or speculation. The experiments of such science must be unlimitedly repeatable under clearly defined experimental conditions.

The term "biological evolution" involves the following aspects:

1. The "autoorganization" of matter (chemical evolution) to a degree capable of supporting life. This chemical autoorganization of matter must be capable of explaining the formation of optically active amino acids, polypeptides, and proteins, as well as the coded, self-replicating, chemical-information-bearing DNA and RNA molecules in biological cells. According to Neodarwinian principles, chemical autoorganization led up to the primitive microspheres and coacervates[1] which are considered to be the most primitive forms of life *(chemical autoorganization)*.

2. The upward development of primitive microspheres and coacervates leading to the evolutionary family tree, as it is conceived by Darwinians to be today. The upward development and formation of present species is supposed

---

[1]*cf* A. E. Wilder Smith: *Creation of Life*. Harold Shaw Publ. (Wheaton, Ill. 60187) p. 67, 81, 91, 99, 103, 108.

to have required millions of years. This phenomenon is known as *biological autoorganization.*

Both chemical *and* biological autoorganization are regarded by Neodarwinian thought as the sole consequences of chance and the laws of nature. Thus the organization of matter up to life and man was neither planned nor guided externally; it "happened" from within the laws of chance and nature. Darwinians purposely stress that no exogenous force or "super-nature" induced the order into chemical or biological autoorganization. According to their theory, everything is to be considered as a result of the interplay between chance and the laws of nature, which alone, allegedly, brought about chemical and biological autoorganization.

General Notes

It is taught in nearly all universities and primary, secondary, and high schools of the East, the West, and the Third World, that man shares common ancestors with animals and plants. Allegedly, all living things stem from a primitive biological primeval cell, which emerged spontaneously from inorganic nonliving materials, that is, through chance and autoorganization, according to the above mentioned principles of chemical evolution. From this primeval cell (microspheres, coacervates, etc.), plants, viruses and bacteria, animals, and man developed spontaneously, with the aid of natural selection in the fight for survival. The entire biological spectrum of all known forms of life allegedly does not witness to a previously conceived teleonomic plan which was then executed in matter. It is believed that all species are witnesses to the power of chance and autoorganization, which, aided by the properties of matter, spontaneously produced the phenomenon that we call life. Before Darwin, it was believed and taught that plan, concept, and intelligence (that is, teleonomy) produced the organization which makes up the machinery of life. Today Neodarwinians believe that chance, the laws of nature, and natural selection provide a sufficient explanation for the phenomenon of life: everything supposedly witnesses to autoorganization and not to external teleonomy.

According to evolutionary theory, chance mutations or chemical alterations within the basic structure of the genetic code provide the driving power behind organic evolution in all forms of life. Most alterations of this type are recognized to be harmful, so that the organism carrying them will experience disadvantages in the fight for survival. On the other hand, it is maintained, a few mutations advantageous to the organism will take place. The carriers of such advantages will be better able to survive, producing more offspring than others carrying detrimental mutations. Thus the happy bearer of advantageous mutations is better able to produce offspring and to survive in the fight for nourishment and habitat.

Since the owners of favorable mutations leave behind more offspring than the owners of detrimental ones, the former survive more frequently, causing a constant rise in the qualitative composition of a species; an "upward" evolution thus becomes automatic and takes place without outside planning.

According to this approach, plants, bacteria, viruses, animals, and humans must attribute their evolution from the primeval cell to their present state to mere chance mutations—having nothing in common with intelligence, ideas, concepts, teleonomy, or planning. According to these same views, no intelligent creator with foresight needs to exist to account for man, animals, or plants. A creator with constructive ideas, executed in the matter of our universe, is therefore no longer an *a priori* necessity since the advent of Darwin's ideas. Allegedly the order reigning in the biological world may be explained with the aid of only two basic concepts: those of matter and chance. The necessity of the postulate of a third basic element in the universe—that of teleonomy, planning, idea, logos, know-how—from now on allegedly no longer exists. Prior to Darwin, most educated people believed that our present universe consisted of three basic elements: matter, energy (which revealed itself in the vibrations of chance movements), and information (planning, ideas, intelligence, teleonomy, or logos). But as the last element was always associated with "spirit" (or "God"), one believed in those days in a "spirit" which acted as creator of matter, energy, and concepts. In order to form life from matter and energy this "spirit" used intelligence, information, planning, or teleonomy (know-how). Today this older belief would be formulated in modern language in the following manner: life consists of energy, matter, and know-how (concept, teleonomy, or information).

Evolution Without Know-How

Evolution is thus basically an attempt to explain the origin of life from matter and energy without the aid of know-how, concept, teleonomy, or exogenous (extra-material) information. It represents an attempt to explain the formation of the genetic code from the chemical components of DNA without the aid of a genetic concept (information) originating outside the molecules of the chromosomes. This is comparable to the assumption that the text of a book originates from the paper molecules on which the sentences appear, and not from any *external* source of information (external, that is, to the paper molecules).

Neodarwinian theory attempts to explain the teleonomy and the systems of life in terms of the endogenous properties of matter and chance and not in terms of any external concept. It was previously believed that the information and the genetic concepts of life were of exogenous origin and that these concepts were imposed onto matter from "outside" (transcendentally). Thus matter carried the "footprints" of the transcendent. Since Darwin, it is generally believed that the information and the concepts behind life express the properties of matter itself and of chance. Hence the genetic "Book of Life," genetic information, stems allegedly from the "paper" on which it is written—the nucleotides, bases, and amino acids which comprise DNA. Chance is believed to have synthesized this genetic information onto matter.

Hence evolutionary theory is plausible and simple, for it eliminates the theoretical necessity of an extramaterial source of the teleonomy of life. For this reason it is attractive to all types of intelligence—the seemingly infinite and apparently insoluble problems of theology and morality can, with its help, be solved at one blow: "How can a God of sufficient intelligence to create the world not only be so cruel as to *permit* war, cancer, injustice, and imperfection, but also to *employ it* as his means of creation by evolution?" Darwinism declares such problems to be meaningless. For according to its tenets there exists neither a God of love or morality, nor a God of amorality. Only chance really exists. The laws of matter, chance, and natural selection alone have created us, and this eliminates such terms as love and morality as problems to be taken seriously. Neodarwinian theory elegantly solves the Gordian knot of problems of a moral and theological type. Chance as the creator destroys creative *morality. If chance is our creator, a universal absolute moral code no longer exists.* The question, "Why does God allow it?"[1a] immediately becomes meaningless, a question that has plagued mankind during thousands of years. No wonder that evolutionary theory is generally attractive—especially among the intelligentsia. Almost the entire intellectual world has accepted it today.

Two Scientific Difficulties in Evolutionary Theory

Yet there still remain some major scientific difficulties which prevent the final victory of Neodarwinian thought—the theory totally lacks experimental or theoretical scientific basis!

1. Paleontology gives no "experimental" evidence for a phylogentic evolution of one species to another, higher one, that is, of transformism. Where are the missing links between, e.g. the whale species and land mammals? Where are the intermediate stages linking the invertebrates with vertebrates? Geological research should have discovered such intermediate stages long ago if they existed

---

[1a]*cf.* A. E. Wilder-Smith, CLP Publishers, San Diego, CA 92115.

in the geological formations. But they just do not exist. Even *Archaeopteryx*, the so-called intermediate stage between reptiles and birds, has been questioned regarding its phylogenetic evolutionary significance and turns out to be far younger geologically than birds.[2]

2. The laws of physics—the laws of thermodynamics—also contradict evolutionary theory. For according to the experimental results on which these laws are based, matter alone tends toward chaos or increased entropy. It does not tend toward autoorganization, even if one irradiates it with photon energy. Only with the aid of teleonomic energy consuming machines, the construction of which require energy *and planning,* can entropy be reduced in matter and order and organization increased. But order and organization are the basis of life. Thus according to the laws of physics it is impossible for matter to have organized itself without the aid of energy and of teleonomic machines!

The scientific, experimental evidence which we possess thus speaks decisively against Darwin's theory of evolution. This fact is confirmed by the news that biochemists have succeeded in experimentally organizing the material components of life in the laboratory in such a manner that simple life has been probably formed from nonlife. I am referring to the work of Sol Spiegelman in the USA. Spiegelman ordered matter with the aid of energy and know-how (and therefore with the aid of all the three previously mentioned components of the universe). He made use of the know-how of machines (enzymes) to form a self-replicating entity. According to the definition of life as a self-replicating entity, he thus created primitive life. But Spiegelman did not create life without know-how

---

[2]Further details concerning missing links: *cf* A. E. Wilder Smith: *Grundlage zu einer neuer Biologie (Basis for a New Biology),* Telos Serie, Hänssler Verlag (Neuhausen-Stuttgart, 1975) p. 14, 87-89. *cf Science News* 112 (Sept. 24, 1977) 198; *Archaeopteryx* has turned out to be far younger than birds.

(teleonomy). And certainly not with the aid of chance alone. Thus from an experimental point of view we now know that matter plus energy plus know-how (or information, teleonomy, logos) can produce life. If this is the case in our present-day laboratories, why should it have been different in the case of the original origin of life (biogenesis)? Is it not an axiom of science that the laws governing matter and energy have remained constant since their formation? Darwin's cancelling out of know-how or logos from the biogenetical equation is experimentally unjustified, *for every attempt at artificially creating life in a laboratory proves that scientists, without exception, attempt to synthesize the machine of life from matter using matter, energy, and know-how* (logos, concept, information, expertise).

Today nobody any longer attempts to create life from matter and energy only. Nobody places the simple material components of life in a mixer, or stirring machine, thus adding nonteleonomic energy until life is formed. This type of nonsense has not been carried out since the days of Pasteur. Today energy *and* know-how (information, concept, logos) are always added. Since this step has been taken (i.e., know-how has been added), scientists have become successful in their attempts to create artificial life. Why should it have been different at biogenesis if the laws governing the autoorganization of matter today have remained constant since the origin of matter? Why should matter plus energy plus chance have been vital at biogenesis, whereas today matter and energy plus know-how are required under the same laws? Can chance be replaced by know-how in the equation to achieve the same result?

The theory of evolution is, of course, a philosophy—a philosophy which promises something "for nothing" (gratis, that is)—a principle which has always been popular among the naive, for it promises the formation and creation of order—of machines—from nonorder without any concept or teleonomy, that is "for nothing." It promises to bring about the creation of life spontaneously using nondirectional energy (without a concept) out of the nonorder of nonliving matter. It promises the formation of the most complex biological machine, the cell—for the biological cell is an incredibly complex metabolic machine —without the necessity of know-how or machine concept. Where in the history of experimental science does one find a postulate for the construction of a *machine* from "raw" matter without concept, know-how, or information —merely by means of autoorganization? Whenever in the history of the world did *a machine* arise spontaneously from matter? Neodarwinism postulates the development through chance and autoorganization of the most refined coding system for a machine (the cell) ever seen. This cell machine is far more complex than any machine ever invented by man. What information engineer would attribute the development of code and code-content to chance? Such a postulate would be refuted immediately in all other areas of science—except the Neodarwinian biology. Plain common sense eliminates such ideas in any other realm of science but biology! But biology retains this plain nonsense in the sole interest of materialistic philosophy.

Chapter 2

Biogenesis By Chance?

The Formation of the Building Blocks of Life

The Formation of the Building Blocks from a Chemical Point of View

Experiments by Miller[1] and others have supported among experts the general conviction that the amino acids, which represent the building blocks and the basis of life, were formed by chance—normal, unguided, nonteleonomic chemical reactions. In the primeval atmosphere of the early earth, consisting mainly of water vapor, ammonia, methane, nitrogen, and carbon dioxide, electrical discharges or lightning took place, whereby small amounts of various biologically essential amino acids were spontaneously synthesized. Miller carried out simulated experiments of this type in the laboratory, and from them he obtained small but definite amounts of the building blocks of life (amino acids) (**I**). According to expert opinion he had thus solved the problem of the origin of the first biologically essential amino acids.

Now, if such amino acids dissolve in water under favorable chemical conditions, any two of them will allegedly combine, releasing a molecule of water and forming a peptide (**II**):

---

[1]S. L. Miller: *Science* 117 (1953) 528: *Journal of Amer. Chem. Soc.* 77 (1955) 2351.

$$\text{(I)} \quad CH_4 + H_2O + NH_3 + \text{energy} \longrightarrow R - \overset{\overset{\displaystyle NH_2}{\displaystyle |}}{C}H - COOH$$

(methane + water + ammonia (matter) + energy (e.g., Lightning) = amino acid

(building block of life)

(II)

$$R - \underset{\underset{\displaystyle NH_2}{\displaystyle |}}{C}H - COOH + R^1 - \underset{\underset{\displaystyle NH_2}{\displaystyle |}}{C}H - COOH \overset{\text{Condensation}}{\underset{}{\rightleftharpoons}} R - \underset{\underset{\displaystyle NH - CO - \underset{\underset{\displaystyle NH_2}{\displaystyle |}}{C}H - R^1 + H_2O}{\displaystyle |}}{C}H - COOH$$

(amino acid 1 + amino acid 2 combine to give peptide + water)

The amino group (NH_2) of the amino acid (R = radical) combines with the carboxy group (COOH) of the second amino acid, releasing HOH (= water, H_2O) to form the peptide. Now on examining the formula for the peptides, one finds that they always carry an additional NH_2 group and a COOH group so that the dipeptide, for example, can combine with a second dipeptide (or monopeptide or amino acid) to form a quadripeptide (or tripeptide, etc.) **(III)**. Again a molecule of water is released during this process.

(III)   R – CH – COOH   + R – CH – COOH
              | |
              NH – CO – CH – R¹   NH – CO – CH – R¹
                         | |
                         NH₂   NH₂

        1   2

                        Condensation
                          reaction

                    R¹   R
                    | |
R – CH – CO – NH – CH – CO – NH – CH – COOH + H₂O
    |
    NH – CO – CH – R¹
              |
              NH₂   ₃

(peptide 1 + peptide 2 combine to give tripeptide 3 plus water)

If a further condensation (as this type of reaction is called) is carried out between polypeptide molecules one finally—after the chain has reached a length of several thousand building blocks (amino acids)—obtains proteins similar to those of life. In the past it was even said that life itself consists of condensation reactions between amino acids with the liberation of water. Thus the proteins of life consist of amino acids of this type, only the chains are often very long. They may contain thousands of amino acid residues.

Now, as many types of amino acids can be obtained spontaneously in a primeval type of atmosphere with the aid of electric discharges—Miller has proven this—and as amino acids in aqueous solution are said to combine spontaneously (according to equations **II** and **III**) to give peptides, polypeptides, and protein-like substances, an experimental basis for spontaneous biogenesis (initial creation of life), according to experts, thus has been established. The building blocks of life (amino acids) and the peptides (basis of proteins) are both produced spontaneously, according to Miller's scheme, from energy and matter with no help from extramaterial teleonomy. Hence many experts and most leading textbooks are convinced that the way has now been cleared for the postulate of a chance spontaneous origin of life on a scientific basis. Given energy and a primeval atmosphere, living protoplasm, followed by the whole tree of life, *must* (this is stressed today) eventually appear spontaneously and automatically. According to Oparin, a microsphere or a coacervate, a primitive cell[2] which begins to replicate—that is to reproduce by means of cell division—will eventually be formed once a sufficient amount of vital protein exists within a primeval ocean. Beyond this stage, natural selection allegedly will provide automatic development without the help of any external teleonomy all the way up to Homo sapiens.

According to this generally accepted scheme, the building blocks of the first cell were thus formed by chance lightning in the primeval atmosphere. Once a colony of living cells existed in a primeval ocean, natural selection took over due to competition between cells (for nourishment and habitat), resulting in an entirely automatic evolution in the Neodarwinian sense of the word, without any outside planning. The cells possessing the most favorable mutations (arising by chance) were dominant and produced more offspring than the cells with less favorable mutations. According to this theory, selection must have led to the highest biological stage of development (Homo sapiens) over millions of years. Thus man, or a similar higher organism, must have automatically arisen through chance and selection in all places where such conditions (chance, energy, and selection) are available. For this reason many Neodarwinians state that man (or an equivalent species of a comparably high level of biological

---

[2]*cf* A. E. Wilder Smith: *Creation of Life,* Chapter 4. (Harold Shaw Publishers, Wheaton) (literature references), CLP Publishers, San Diego, CA 92115.

development) must, and will with time, develop on other suitable planets also. Everywhere in the universe (on other planets) where the purely physical and chemical prerequisites exist, evolutionary processes will take place leading to a highly developed form of life. For this reason life—and also intelligent life—is sought on other planets and in other galaxies. This is the real purpose of the Mars probes, which attempted to ascertain whether biological life exists on that planet. According to Neo-darwinian theory, various types of life should be evident in all those situations where the purely material conditions for development of life are fulfilled.

Now we must test the scientific feasibility of the above generally accepted propositions.

Spontaneous Biogenesis in Primeval Oceans?

Could biogenesis have occurred spontaneously from amino acids and polypeptides according to the above-mentioned equations (**I - III**)? Biology textbooks state nearly unanimously that this is the case. But even a superficial chemical examination of the equations provides a definitive negative reply to this question. How is this possible, when textbooks practically unanimously teach the contrary?

On examining the equations, the above reactions are found to be reversible—that is, they take place forward or backward depending on experimental conditions (hence the sign $\rightleftharpoons$). The direction in which the reaction takes place depends on the concentration of reagents on both sides of the equation. For the sake of simplicity, we shall consider only one of the reagents—the water which is formed, i.e. released during this reaction. If the molecules of water which have been released by the condensation reaction on the right hand side of the equation are removed as soon as they appear, and their concentration is thus reduced in the reacting mixture, the entire reaction should tend toward the right hand side, and the theoretical yield of peptides—as represented in the equation—

be obtained.   Conversely by adding large amounts of water (instead of removing water) to the reacting mixture, no peptides or only very few will be formed (depending on the amount of water):   instead, the initial reagents, amino acids, are obtained (*cf* **II**).   Thus, if excess water is present in the reacting mixture, peptide synthesis does not take place, equilibrium remains on the side of the initial reagents, the amino acids, which are the building blocks of life.   This phenomenon is covered by the law of mass action: it is valid for all reversible reactions. Briefly said: in reactions of this type, synthesis of poly-peptides from amino acids does not take place in the presence of excess water.

The consequence of this well-known fact of organic chemistry is important: concentrations of amino acids will combine only in minute amounts, if they combine at all in a primeval ocean providing excess water, to form polypeptides. Any amounts of polypeptide which might be formed will be broken down into their initial components (amino acids) by the excess water.   *The ocean is thus practically the last place on this or any other planet where the proteins of life could be formed spontaneously from amino acids.*   Yet nearly all textbooks of biology teach this nonsense to support evolutionary theory and spon-taneous biogenesis.   It requires a very great unfamiliarity with organic chemistry not to take into consideration the above-mentioned facts when proposing postulates for biogenesis . . . or has materialistic Neodarwinian philoso-phy overwhelmed us to such an extent that we forget or overlook the well known facts of science and of chemistry in order to support this philosophy?   We shall return to this topic again at a later stage.[2a]

[2a]This scheme omits activation of amino acids by ATP and com-bination with t.RNA. See p. 162.

Properties of the Building Blocks of Life: The Amino Acids and Their Chirality

Approximately twenty amino acids comprise the basic

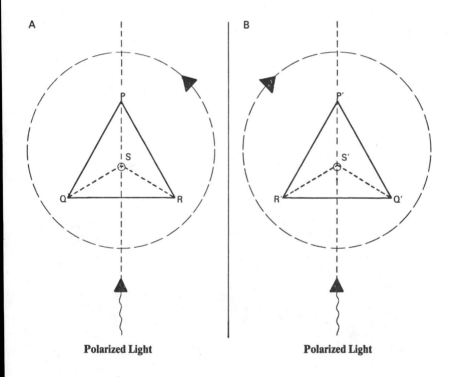

Figure 1. Representation of Chirality on the structural model of two molecules. *A.* Tetrahedron viewed vertically from above, represented two-dimensionally. *P, Q, R,* and *S* denote vertices of the tetrahedron and represent the four valencies of the carbon atom. The carbon atom *S* lies at the center of the basis triangle (three-dimensionally: the vertex opposite the basis triangle). In this molecule (A) the plane of polarized light is rotated to the left (counterclockwise). *B.* Tetrahedron viewed vertically from above, represented two-dimensionally. Description as A; note however, that *Q* and *R* are reversed w.r.t. A. The plane of polarized light is rotated to the right (clockwise) by this molecule (B).

building blocks of life from a material point of view. Without these, life as we know it today could neither originate nor exist. Some of these amino acids can, under certain circumstances, be formed in the primeval atmosphere through chance lightning, as we have already discovered. But to state, as many experts do, that these amino acids which are formed by chance can be used to build living protoplasm is certainly grossly erroneous in principle, for they are for such purposes, in fact, entirely useless. Without exception all Miller's amino acids are completely unsuitable for any type of spontaneous biogenesis. *And the same applies to all and any randomly formed substances and amino acids which form racemates.* This statement is categorical and absolute and cannot be affected by special conditions.

Now we must explain why the above statement applies. The carbon atoms which are present in all amino acids may be regarded as the center of a tetrahedron (of a figure bounded by four isosceles triangles). Geometrically, the four valencies of the carbon atom are directed toward the four corners (P, Q, R, S) of the tetrahedron. Schematically, this may be represented in the following manner (A and B), where P, Q, R, S represent various substituents on the carbon valencies (Fig. 1).

From a purely chemical point of view, A and B are, of course, identical structures. But A is the mirror image of B—and B, of course, of A. Now if A and B represent structural models of real molecules, a plane of polarized light passing through A will be rotated in the opposite direction to the one in which the same light will rotate on passing through B. The mirror in the middle represents the mirror image structure of the two molecules. Tetrahedron A is a mirror image of tetrahedron B. Therefore A can never be imposed on B so that P, Q, R, and S are all congruent—just as it is impossible to place a left hand glove over a right hand glove so that all fingers and both thumbs are congruent. Left hand and right hand gloves are mirror images, because my left hand is a mirror image of my right hand. The only difference between A and B lies in the spatial arrangements of the components and not in the chemical composition, which remains identical in both cases.

Two otherwise chemically identical molecules possessing mirror-image structures constitutes *chirality* in chemical language. Thus two molecules of which one is the mirror image of the other, will differ only in their spatial structure and not in their chemical analysis. On building long chains of molecules possessing different stereostructures (chirality), it will be immediately clear that any long chain consisting of laevorotary molecules (l-form from Lat. laevus, left) will differ structurally from any chain of dextrorotary molecules (d-form, from Lat. dexter, right)— or from mixtures of both (dl-forms). A long chain consisting of left hand gloves would look different three-dimensionally to a chain consisting of right hand gloves or of a mixture of both. The chemical contents of both chains would be identical, but the stereostructure of the chains would differ.

Thus, when long chains of proteins are built up from amino acids—such as, for example, the proteins of the human brain—the stereostructure (the chirality) of the amino acids concerned plays an important role. The three-dimensional properties (chirality) of the amino acids involved determine the properties of the resulting proteins: *dextrorotary* proteins lead to completely different protein chains to those produced from *laevorotary* ones—or to the ones produced from a mixture of dextrorotary and laevorotary amino acids, i.e. of racemates (dl-forms).

It has been found that the proteins which contribute to living protoplasm are, with very few exceptions, laevorotary. Dextrorotary amino acids and proteins occur very seldom in living protoplasm, for they form proteins which do not fit into the metabolism of living organisms. Often proteins consisting of dextrorotary amino acids are lethal. Thus laevorotary chirality in the amino acids of life is an absolute necessity; dextrorotary forms are simply incapable of supporting life. But this chiral specificity goes even further. Whereas the amino acids of the living proteins are laevorotary, all nucleic acids exhibit an exclusive dextro configuration.[3]

Cell metabolism may be compared to one chemical substance entering another, just as a left hand enters a left hand glove. In the cell the "left hands" are coupled together through the thumb and little fingers to produce long chains of left hands. These may be likened to the long protein chains of life. The long chains of left hands may be thought of as entering into corresponding long chains of left handed gloves, also coupled through thumb and little finger. Cell metabolism consists of chains of thousands of left hands entering into long chains of coupled left handed gloves. This process may be thought of as vibratory and it must take place easily.

If in a chain of 10,000 left hands entering into a chain of 10,000 left handed gloves even as much as one right handed glove appears, this one right handed glove can stop the whole vibratory process of long glove chain receiving the long hand chain. Any adventitious right handed gloves and hands will stop exclusively left handed chain systems from entering into each other, thus bringing the whole metabolic process to a standstill. One right handed hand or glove will be sufficient to upset the whole spatial arrangement of systems of this type. It will be easily seen that mixtures of right handedness and left handedness in such chains will never be able to produce a "fit" for metabolism, which is the basic reason why racemates (mixtures of left handedness and right handedness) can never offer any basis at all for the metabolism of life. Therefore Miller's racemates are useless as a basis for biogenesis.

How can we determine which molecules are laevorotary and which are dextrorotary? On passing polarized light (light waves which all oscillate in one plane) through a solution of amino acids exhibiting the left configuration, the plane of polarized light will be rotated to the left (in

---

[3]cf e.g. M. Eigen and Rothild Winkler. Das Spiel, R. Piper Verlag (München/Zürich, 1975), 142.

some circumstances, depending upon substitution, to the right). The opposite chirality turns the plane of polarized light to the right (in some circumstances, depending upon substitution, to the left).

From the above it is obvious that amino acids which are to act as the building blocks of life at biogenesis must exhibit the correct chirality. For biogenesis to take place, *all building blocks* (amino acids) of living protoplasm must be laevorotary. It is very important to stress this point—all building block molecules involved in the synthesis of vital proteins must be "optically pure" and "left"—that is, they must be laevorotary without any traces of dextrorotary isomers. In this respect living protoplasm is very fussy: it demands absolutely pure "fare." If even very small amounts of amino acid molecules of the dextrorotary type are present, proteins of a different three-dimensional structure are formed, which are unsuitable for life's metabolism. Often such proteins can even be fatal to life. Our comparison with hands and gloves illustrates this point.

When a living cell is offered nourishment in the form of a 50%/50% mixture of laevo- and dextrorotary amino acids (that is a racemate, dl), the cell will accept the laevorotary type and incorporate it within its protoplasm. Certain cells are also capable of making use of dextrorotary forms. First they carefully break them down and then rebuild them in the laevorotary form. Only after this conversion are these amino acids taken up by the living proteins in the cell and incorporated. But dextrorotary protein forms, as such, are useless or even toxic to the cell. Dextrorotary forms from racemates are never converted into laevorotary forms spontaneously and chemically, but break down, and therefore conversion by a cell does take place.

Other interesting phenomena exist which are connected with chirality. Certain organisms such as penicillium notatum (the cell which synthesizes penicillin) protect themselves against invaders by synthesizing dextrorotary acids, which kill the "enemy." Penicillin itself represents just such a biological poison against invasion. One of its components is a dextrorotary acid.

Thus the biological cell "understands" the metabolical treatment of laevo- and dextrorotary acids. It can even break down dextrorotary forms and rebuild them in the laevorotary forms for its own purposes. But it is impossible that the primeval cell was built up from dextrorotary or from a 50/50 mixture of dextro- and laevorotary amino acids (from a racemate, that is). At biogenesis, the vital proteins as we know them today could not have been formed from racemates or from dextrorotary amino acids.

Now we are in a position to support our original statement—that the primeval cell never developed from a dl mixture of amino acids (as alleged by Miller), which in turn was formed by chance through lightning in the primeval atmosphere. All building blocks of life—amino acids or also other asymmetric compounds (substances which can produce a mirror image) which are formed by lightning (by chance) or other natural, nonbiological processes—appear as racemates only, that is, in 50% laevorotary and 50% dextrorotary forms. The amino acids produced by Miller are exclusively and entirely racemates, and hence basically and absolutely unsuited for the metabolism of life. Under no circumstances whatsoever is a racemate (dl-form) capable of forming living proteins or live-supporting protoplasm of any sort. The spatial configuration of a racemate is basically not suitable for the synthesis of life according to modern biochemical knowledge, as we have seen from the glove comparison. In order to obtain life-supporting protoplasm and vital proteins, a source of optically pure l-amino acids must be available. Mixtures of l- and d-forms do not provide this satisfactory source. *Lightning and chance can, on principle, never produce only pure laevorotary forms;* they produce racemates only—exactly 50% d- and exactly 50% l-forms—and are therefore unsuitable for life's proteins.

At their origin the building blocks of life must all have been of purely left chirality. But chance and all natural, nonliving, or nonasymmetrical chemical processes provide racemates only. Here we are not speaking of enzymes which are often asymmetrical and optically active and can therefore produce specific chirality. Thus Miller and his colleagues provided *no building blocks of any use* for the synthesis of life by the action of lightning and chance on a simulated primeval atmosphere, but only racemates unsuited to life. *No* method is known to present-day science by means of which inorganic random processes resolve from racemates pure laevo- or pure dextrorotary forms. Lightning, primeval atmosphere and inorganic, random processes cannot realize such optical resolution, either from a theoretical or an experimental aspect, for no *chemical differences* exist between simple l- and d- amino acids. The only differences between them rest on a three-dimensional basis. Thus chance alone is, on principle, incapable of effecting the optical resolution required for the synthesis of life from amino acids. An already existing optically active center, such as that in brucine, strychnine, or a similar substance, must be introduced into the reaction to effect optical resolution. But chance never provides an originally optically active center—*for this reason alone chance cannot, either on theoretical or practical grounds,* produce a living cell! Why biology uses the l- forms and not the d- forms is not known—theoretically, the d- form would be feasible if it were optically pure.

Hence it is scientifically erroneous to state that Miller's experiments have made possible the synthesis of life by natural processes (organic chemistry) and chance. Here we are dealing with a misleading half-truth, for Miller, as well as his colleagues after him, only produced racemates which are just as useless for biogenesis as no amino acids at all. It is incomparably more difficult (and requires much more know-how) to produce optically pure forms of an amino acid than to synthesize its racemates.

For more than 80 years, reputable scientists have attempted in vain to produce optically pure amino acids by random inorganic methods without involving life or other previously present optically active centers in any way. If someone could make progress in this problem, which is fundamental to solving the mystery of biogenesis, he would probably become an immediate candidate for a Nobel prize! For herein lies a major obstacle blocking the scientific credibility of present-day materialistic theories concerning biogenesis. Probably for this reason modern text books often do not even mention this major difficulty of chirality. Their authors are often supporters of the materialistic point of view on biogenesis. They know that the problem posed by racemates greatly detracts from the concept of biogenesis through chance and natural random chemical processes. For this reason the significance of this phenomenon is often omitted or left unclarified in text books for the young!

Over the years various scientists have tried to optically resolve racemates and to separate the l- from the d- forms, by producing amino acids through chance chemical processes on optically active surfaces which are optically active without the presence of an atomic asymmetrical center. Crystals of quarz were chosen to provide an optically active surface, but to no avail. Scientists have tried to obtain optically active amino acids from racemates in the presence of circularly polarized light. They believed that one optical form would be destroyed more quickly than the other by the circularly polarized light and that the isomers could thus be separated. Yet all the experiments were more or less fruitless—only negligible amounts of optical activity were observed. It must be borne in mind that for the synthesis of life to occur, practically 100% optical purity is required in as many as 20 different amino acids. Never has an optically pure specimen been obtained by any inorganic random reactions. For these and other reasons, spontaneous biogenesis has remained an *experimental* impossibility to the present day. Theoretical considerations also support this negative experimental result.[3a]

So we can only conclude that the actual building blocks of life at biogenesis—approximately 20 optically pure amino acids—were *not* synthesized by means of inorganic, random processes. Accordingly, Miller's experiments have little in common with real biogenesis, although text books describe the experiments as if they provided the last link in the chain of evidence for chance biogenesis. To claim that Miller has provided the first step for spontaneous biogenesis involves a willful misleading of the uninformed general public in the interests of biased materialistic philosophy. The facts are purposely concealed in order to render plausible a materialistic philosophy of life. Thus science is manipulated in the interests of popular materialistic philosophies.

Of course, optically pure laevorotary amino acids can be produced in a laboratory. I have synthesized by the kilogram optically pure alanine, as well as α-amino-butyric acid and many other similar compounds, but never by chance. With the aid of know-how and a prior asymmetric center, this is easily accomplished, but never through chance (non-know-how). Complicated chemical processes are required to carry out this synthetic puzzle. To obtain resolution, a previously established optically active center is required, which is of course *never* produced by chance. Any educated chemist will smile if chance is mentioned in this context.

Manfred Eigen's Explanation for the Origin of the Chirality Required by Biogenesis

No direct spontaneous biogenesis can ensue from a racemic mixture of amino acids, as the chirality required by the vital proteins is not available. *The spatially orientated receptor systems of the cell would not function.* If, however, a living cell were nevertheless formed from a racemic mixture, it would have very little in common with the forms of life with which we are familiar today. Life, as we know it today, depends on chirality and *spatially orientated receptors*—but spatially orientated receptors are absolutely dependent on chirality for their functions.

Eigen inquires why no peaceful coexistence of l- and d-forms of life occurs in nature.[4] Why do we find exclusively

---

[3a]*cf.* W. Thiemann, Institut für Physikalische Chemie der Kermforschungsanlage Jülich, G.M.B.H. Jülich (1974), see p. 156.

[4]Eigen and Winkler (Footnote 2, p. 57 of this book).

l-forms of amino acids and d-forms of nucleic acids? The answer is clear to every biologist: life is absolutely dependent on spatial structures and chirality, though we do not know why l-amino acids rather than d-isomers were chosen. Eigen's replies to this problem are interesting: (a) It is one of the characteristics of a self-replicating system, he writes, that both optical forms cannot coexist. Although this sentence is, in itself, completely accurate, it of course does not say much to a layman. (b) Because natural selection dictates survival on the basis of "all-or-none," writes Eigen, the domination of only one form, left or right, was simply a question of time.

This statement is important, for here Eigen has said something with which few molecular biologists can agree, for he states in effect that both laevo- and dextrorotary amino acids and their mixtures were in the past capable of living. This statement represents, of course, pure philosophy and not experimental science, for experimentally no racemate cell exists or can exist as we know life today, which fact Eigen also confirms under (a). According to his statement (b) racemates and dextrorotary proteins could still have taken part in spontaneous biogenesis. Thus Eigen contradicts not only himself but the majority of biochemists, too. If this were really the case, racemates or d-forms would react differently with themselves and their environments than l-forms, for the drug/receptor or agonist/antagonist relationships would be affected to such an extent by the various chiralities that the entire cell metabolism would have to be changed. Thus a species of life different from that we know today would be required. Point (a) is certainly correct from every point of view—*it is a characteristic of life that both forms cannot coexist peacefully*. But how then could it develop in one place from a racemic mixture? All the spatial proportions governing the agonist/antagonist relationships would become chaotic where nonuniform chirality prevailed. Point (b) assumes that the species we know today were produced from racemates by spontaneous biogenesis, which would indeed be more than problematic; for (1) according to experimental evidence racemic life could not exist at biogenesis; (2) theoretically it certainly cannot exist; (3) natural selection operating to separate l- and d- forms could only occur once racemic life existed.

We can draw two conclusions from Eigen's statements: firstly it is certainly true, as Eigen states, that the character of a self-replicating system does not permit blurring of the boundaries set by chirality. Thus a functioning, self-replicating cellular metabolic system could not tolerate any peaceful coexistence of d- and l- forms. Racemates could not initiate biogenesis of present-day life, for the stereochemical conditions on which life, as we know it, depends, would not be fulfilled. The second conclusion is: because *no* existing life is based on racemates, it is out of the question to speak of natural selection as *acting* on this life to decide whether the d- or the l- form emerges victorious in the fight for survival. *Where there is no life, there is, of course, no natural selection either.* If racemates as such cannot support life, no *scientist* can claim that natural selection in this "non-life" induced optical resolution. If in a race all the participants are lying dead on the starting line, how can one speak of any sort of victory in the selection provided by a race? For this reason selection based on racemates cannot magically induce optical resolution and therefore it has never taken place.

These facts must have been overlooked by Eigen and others. For this reason their explanations of the origin of the optical activity of life are tautological.

In the world of fairy tales, many difficult situations exist. The hero is killed by the witch. Or the beloved, beautiful, and only daughter dies of a fever which a wicked witch has induced by a spell. Now the solution to all these problems is always provided by the magic wand—the magic wand is fetched and waved over the wound or the corpse and behold! All is well again! The dead princess happily rises up again and the wicked witch explodes in a puff of pitch-black smoke.

Present-day biology has also discovered a magic wand which solves all biological and chemical problems with one wave of the wand. Does the origin of the most complicated machinery of a protein molecule need explanation? Do we need to explain how optical isomers are formed? Do we wish to know why the wings of certain butterflies are decorated with eagle's eyes? The magic wand called chance and natural selection will without exception explain all of these miracles. It explains the origin of the most complicated biological machine—the enzymatic protein molecule. The explanation is fabulous—machines are formed of their own accord, spontaneously, just as the waving of a magic wand would demand. The same wand explains the billions of teleonomical electrical contacts in the brain. It explains the almost infinitely complicated wiring of the computer called the brain. This wand-type fallacy stems from one single misconception only: it believes, as it were, that the *competition* between car manufacturers for a place in the market *develops* new cars. It forgets that competition only *sorts* out previously existing plans and concepts without teleonomically *designing* them. Natural selection is even supposed to undertake optical resolution, even in those places where neither life nor selection exist! Natural selection working on chance (nonteleonomy) is the modern magic wand!

We are faced with one of the greatest unsolved biological problems still existing today. The proteins of life must have originated from optically pure l- amino acids from a program capable of producing them. Similarly, d- acids derived from optical resolution, or a program capable of such, must have formed nucleic acids. Despite claims of the Establishment, natural selection cannot have played a part in the biogenetically required optical resolution of d- and l- forms, as natural selection is impossible *before* life.

Thus we must pose the original question again: where were the optically active substances taken from to synthesize the first optically pure proteins and nucleic acids? From pattern recognition or a suitable program? It is certain that the amino acids which Miller and his colleagues synthesized by means of lightning and chance in a primeval atmosphere were totally useless for biogenesis— even more useless than car tools for the construction of a precision watch—for they were all racemates.

Laboratory experiments can of course provide indications regarding the synthesis of the optically active amino acids required for biogenesis. Experiments should enlighten us in our concept of biogenetical procedure. For this reason we now look to experiments to provide the only safe basis for theoretical considerations. In order to obtain optical activity from a racemate in the laboratory, the first step entails the incorporation of an optically active center—an optically active molecule—into the racemic system. A racemic acid is combined with a laevo- or dextrorotary base, such as strychnine or brucine. In this manner two different, distinguishable substances are formed: (a) l-acid/l-brucine; (b) d-acid/l-brucine. The substances (a) and (b) often exhibit different solubilities, so that they can be separated by crystallization. After separating (a) and (b) by crystallization, they are separately broken down into their components: (a) provides the l-acid as well as brucine; (b) provides the d-acid and brucine.

In order to resolve a racemate into its optically active components one needs to (1) introduce a molecule which already exhibits optical activity into the racemic system, (2) use know-how to induce resolution, and (3) provide energy.

A living cell is capable of producing large amounts of optically active substances. It possesses the prerequisite asymmetrical centers. Animals and plants both exhibit this capacity. They possess in their genetical code the information or know-how, as well as the chirality required to build optically active materials. Cell metabolism provides the energy. Thus optical activity is obtained experimentally and scientifically: know-how in the form of code or optically active enzymes, coupled with energy, is required for this process of optical resolution. Previously existing optical activity is needed. Biological enzymes provide the previously existing optical activity, and the genetic code provides the know-how. But neither optical activity nor know-how ever originated randomly.

However all this does not solve our problem—where the

optically pure amino acids required for the biogenetical synthesis of the first cell originated. Eigen's suggestion, that biology began with racemates—with "racemic life"— is not accepted by most biologists, as we have already stated. For this reason, optical activity or a program for it must have been present prior to biogenesis and not afterwards. So we assume that primeval life developed from optically active materials or program for them which were available before and during the appearance of life. The obtaining of optical activity thus requires energy, a previously existing optically active center, and know-how. Sources of energy present no problem even previous to biogenesis. But where can we obtain an optically active center and programmed know-how before biogenesis in an inorganic world?

The problem may be expressed more simply. We know that three prerequisites are required for the experimental formation of optical activity: know-how, energy, and an already existing optically active center or a program for the same. However, we can manage without this asymmetrical center under certain experimental conditions— although this is not done in normal laboratory procedure —as we shall now see.

When Pasteur worked with tartaric acid, he found that some tartaric acid crystals adopted one certain shape and others again were differently shaped. He separated the two forms from each other by placing them under the microscope and physically separating the crystals with a pair of forceps. So he used his eye—and his intelligence— to undertake a separation of isomers on the basis of physical differentiation—an illustration of *pattern recognition* based on know-how. The different forms of the tartaric acid crystals stem from the fact that two asymmetric centers are present in each molecule of tartaric acid. In cases where only one center is available per molecule, Pasteur's method of differentiation would not be applicable because he could not have exercised pattern recognition under a normal microscope. Had Pasteur been able to *see the molecules,* he would have been in a position to do so and to have effected a true optical resolution.

Once optical resolution has been carried out by means of pattern recognition, the optical activity thus gained would be used to separate other racemates according to normal laboratory procedure. Thus with the aid of know-how and pattern recognition we have now provided one of the prerequisites for original optical resolution. Previous optical activity, therefore, does not appear to be absolutely necessary—in some cases intelligence, pattern recognition, or know-how can provide an alternative.

We are now in a position to approach our original problem. Where do the optically active building blocks (the optically active amino acids) of biogenesis originate? Know-how, pattern recognition, and energy must originally have provided them. Of course, the required energy presents no problem. However, the inclusion of know-how and pattern recognition as a third component for biogenesis, together with matter and energy, does present difficulties to modern man—who is tied to materialistic philosophy by brainwashing from primary school onward. Matter, time, and space themselves do not carry any know-how, intelligence, pattern recognition, or teleonomy within an inorganic world (the sphere of materialism). But know-how, pattern recognition, and intelligence are required to undertake original optical resolution, and therefore to build machines such as enzymatic protein molecules. This means that plan, teleonomy, pattern recognition, and know-how must have been available at biogenesis in order to account for optical activity. Chirality is impossible without original know-how, pattern recognition, or teleonomy. As pattern recognition is not present in our inorganic space-time continuum, it must have resided outside it at biogenesis!

As we know of no place within our dimensions of time and space harboring know-how or pattern recognition (or teleonomy), and as know-how is absolutely essential for the origin of life and the development of optical activity (just as know-how is absolutely essential for the development of any and all machines, including enzymatic protein molecules), we must as scientists assume that extramaterial know-how, concept, or teleonomy was somehow involved in the original optical resolution at biogenesis.

Different opinions are possible regarding the source of this required know-how not resident in inorganic matter. Aldous Huxley (the materialist!) imagined a universal "think-tank" to overcome this point. We shall later return to this problem. Know-how, pattern recognition, intelligence, and teleonomy are naturally all closely related. They are not only needed to resolve isomers optically, they are used to build all sorts of machines, for machines are by definition teleonomic institutions. Eigen himself illustrates very nicely that enzymatic proteins are small machines, just as much as a car is a machine—a *teleonomic* machine: such proteins may be regarded as the smallest machines known to man. They cut, weld, exchange, sort, transport, and transform molecules, and each protein or enzyme serves a certain purpose. Hence Monod designates them as teleonomic structures! Their structure conforms to no aesthetic principles. Expedience provides the only yardstick—just as in the case of many machines designed and constructed by man.[5]

Thus, protein molecules (proteins, enzymes) are above all teleonomic structures (machines) just as if they had been designed by man. The "designing" introduces teleonomy, pattern recognition, expedience, concept, and know-how into the picture of biogenesis. Optical resolution requires chemical know-how—just as the construction of a machine, even of a protein machine, requires teleonomy.

For these reasons a genuine and informed scientist can today no longer believe in the origin of life through chance and without teleonomy. Behind biogenesis we do not find chance, but its complete antithesis: concept, teleonomy, pattern recognition, or know-how. The construction of protein-machines, as well as the separation of optical antipodes, requires the antithesis of chance, which we call know-how. Experimentally scientifically orientated

---

[5]Quot. by Eigen and Winkler (Footnote 2, p. 57 of this book).

thought forces us to this conclusion. Of course, the source of this know-how or teleonomy has not yet been determined by scientific methods, but we do know that inorganic matter is not teleonomic. We are familiar with matter and the dimensions of time and space to such an extent that it is improbable that this purely material continuum of space and time incorporates the required know-how. The second law of thermodynamics denies the presence of *intrinsic* teleonomy in matter. Thus, I personally assume that concept, know-how, intelligence, and teleonomy are not only to be found within the human mind, but outside our space and time continuum also.

It is highly unlikely that we shall discover the mechanism of biogenesis and biology as long as we attribute the origin of biological protein machines and the optical resolution of amino acids to chance, rather than to its antithesis (know-how). The same dilemma appears everywhere in modern biology—even where the development of the genetic code is also attributed to chance. I have described this dilemma and its consequences elsewhere.[6]

Further Synthetical Difficulties

"Proteins cannot be formed from amino acids by a simple reversal of proteolysis, the reaction equilibrium lies well in favor of hydrolysis and not condensation." (*cf Kurzes Lehrbuch der Biochemie fur Mediziner and Naturwissenschaftler,* by Professor Dr. P. Karlson, Georg Thieme, Verlag, Stuttgart, 1966, p. 115.) In order to make possible a condensation of this kind from amino acids to proteins, the amino acids must be activated, that is, brought to a higher group transfer potential. This requires energy which, in the cell, is supplied by adenosine triphosphate (ATP). For every amino acid there exists at least one specific activating enzyme and at least one speci-

---

[6]A. E. Wilder Smith: *Demission des wissenschaftlichen Materialismus.* Telos Verlag (Neuhausen-Stuttgart, 1976).

fic transfer-RNA.[7] The substances which allow in the cell the execution of this highly complex mechanism (the coupling of amino acids to proteins) are, then, enzymes and transfer-RNA, neither of which can be imagined to have been formed from methane, ammonia, and water vapor by the agency of lightning strokes in a primeval atmosphere and a primeval soup.

---

[7]See also: *Biochemistry, The Molecular Basis of Cell Structure and Function,* Albert L. Lehninger, the Johns Hopkins University School of Medicine, Worth Publishers, Inc., 70 Fifth Avenue, New York, 1972, pp. 693-694.

Chapter 3

Biogenesis By Chance?

Linkage of The Building Blocks

The Standard Scheme

So random chemical reactions do not produce building blocks of life that might be of any use, hence no basic materials are available for materialistically orientated biogenesis. Although we cannot allot any useful building blocks of life to materialistic philosophy, we must analyze further biogenetical steps in their theoretical scheme in order to understand it as an entity. Which are the next steps in biogenesis as Oparin and most textbooks describe them? Once these have been established, we shall find it easier to understand Darwinian philosophy, and we shall recognize its scientific failings more clearly.

As already mentioned (*cf* equations **II** and **III**, Chapter 2), certain optically active amino acids must combine to form chains in order to provide vital proteins. Each linking of two amino acid molecules releases one molecule of water. This chain formation with a release of water is called "condensation."

Such linkages, however, constitute reversible reactions which can either form peptides and proteins or revert to their original components. They can either "go forward," leading to peptides and proteins, or "backward," reverting to their original components. The direction of the reaction is determined by the relative concentrations of the initial components and the products (*cf* Chapter 2). Whether the equation **II** will run forward, forming peptides, or backward, giving amino acids, depends on the experimental conditions and the concentration of the reactants. For this reason, both sides of equation **II** are not connected by ═════ but by ⇌. This sign indicates that the equation may, according to experimental conditions, run forward or backward. A "reversible" reaction is set up in this manner. Many reactions of substances involving carbon are reversible. As previously indicated, the consequences of this fact are of great significance for the problem of biogenesis.

As we have seen, the presence of excess water prevents the formation of proteins. The building blocks of life, the individual amino acids which have been formed in a primeval ocean, will not be synthesized further into proteins. Excess water breaks down the proteins and prevents their formation. So we shall repeat the only logical consequence of this fact, for it is of importance in further stages of this chapter: *A primeval soup in a primeval ocean is the very last place in which a spontaneous biogenesis by means of condensation of the above kind can occur.* Thus the myth of a random, spontaneous formation of vital proteins fails on its first step—the laws of organic chemistry wreck it. Today spontaneous biogenesis is only supported because it conforms to the present materialistic philosophy of life.

As we have already seen, racemic amino acids supplied by chance and lightning are of no use to spontaneous biogenesis. But even if laevorotary amino acids were available in a primeval ocean, this would not provide any vital proteins in the primeval ocean. Reversibility forces the required reactions to act analytically (destructively) instead of synthetically (constructively). Energy potential levels and the role of ATP confirm this.

The Standard Scheme Is Somewhat Modified

A few scientists have, of course, become aware of the difficulty provided by this reversibility of organic reactions and by excess water, although these facts are still not included in certain textbooks for schools. Once this problem has been recognized it can, of course, be solved. A minor alteration of the entire scheme suffices.

When a volcano breaks through the surface of the ocean, glowing lava erupts which then comes into contact with the water while it is still hot. A crust is formed between the lava and the water, where the water continually evaporates due to the heat of the lava. Now if the sea water continually evaporates on such a crust due to the heat of the warm lava, any existing amino acids dissolved in the sea water will be precipitated. The conditions causing this concentration of amino acids on the crust are dehydrating; water is evaporated. So here conditions exist which would favor the formation of peptides—water stemming from the linking of amino acids into peptides (and also from the ocean) is removed from the reaction system. Thus the synthetic reaction converting amino acids into proteins and peptides should now take place. The analytical (breaking down) reaction back to the building blocks of life, the amino acids, will take place less, due to the absence of excess water. Because of the removal of water (evaporation through lava heat), peptides and proteins should be formed here rapidly. The reversibility of the reaction has been terminated by evaporation with the aid of heat. Here, even high yields of protein could be expected from the alleged building blocks of life (which supposedly were originally formed by chance through lightning in the primeval atmosphere).

Now we must pose an important question: Will such proteins be capable of life? The amino acids available to such a system are, unluckily, racemates. So they will form proteins incapable of life. Under the proposed conditions the problem of spontaneous formation of proteins has been solved, but the resulting proteins are not those of life, hence the materialistic scheme must be altered a second time.

The Standard Scheme Is Further Modified

We are all aware of the fact that with the help of certain

precautionary measures the hatching of a chicken from its egg can be prevented. Before putting the 13 eggs under the hen, they are simply boiled for five minutes! Then the hen faithfully sits on them for the required three weeks, but no chicks will emerge. The proteins and the other vital materials are irreversibly "denatured" or coagulated by the heat of the boiling water. The protein becomes solid and acquires a spatially denatured form which can no longer support life. Regrettably this denaturing through heat is normally irreversible; it cannot very easily be undone.

So if proteins are formed from amino acids in a primeval ocean by lava heat (to evaporate the water), any proteins which have been formed will simultaneously be denatured by heat during their formation. Such denatured proteins are useless for biogenesis.

Strong chemicals, such as concentrated sulphuric acid can also remove water just like heat. Regrettably, methods of this type would also involve certain disadvantages—water-removing substances are difficult to find in primeval oceans! Firstly, such substances tend to break down proteins and other materials into their building blocks: into amino acids in the case of proteins. Thus they would reverse the entire synthesis of life—*if* this had ever taken place! Secondly, they tend to denature or coagulate the sensitive vital proteins, just as heat does. Even if water evaporated off without heat and the proteins were not denatured, they would still be useless racemates.

So the modified, adapted scheme does not aid us any further either on the way to a spontaneous formation of life. (In most text books of biogenesis these important facts are not mentioned.) If a spontaneous origin of life took place on this planet, a "primeval soup" would still present one of the most improbable sites for this event.

The fact remains that the primeval cell never could have built its proteins with the aid of spontaneous chance reactions and of amino acids synthesized from lightning in the primeval atmosphere. The modern cell does not synthesize its proteins with the aid of chance organic chemistry either, but through most strictly genetically programmed, coded biochemical processes. *If modern science provides us with insight into the biogenetical science of the past, and thus of original biogenesis* (which most scientists assume), *then the primeval cell must also have formed its optically active proteins with the aid of similar programming and similar coding—* that is with teleonomy and know-how—and not with the aid of *nonprogramming,* that is of chance or nonteleonomy.

This insight into the chemistry of living protein synthesis has been mandatory for the discovery of the genetic code. It is high time that it influenced our concepts concerning the mechanism of original biogenesis.

If programming and not its antithesis—chance—represents the principle behind present-day life, then the only question remaining is "where did the original programming at archebiopoesis, in the primeval cell, originate?"

Today the cell is *programmed* for all synthesis—and does not "the present provide the key to the past," according to modern scientific (especially geological) philosophy? Today a program is developed from a code or a concept. If this is the case today, and if today provides the key to the past, then at biogenesis the original program of the primeval cell must also have been developed from a code or worked out from a concept.

Thus we must ask ourselves again whether chance is capable of programming and concept making originally and successfully. It is clear that programming can be modified by chance or even destroyed by it. No one questions this fact. We are only asking ourselves if a primeval cell could be constructed from biogenesis onward by a program formed with the aid of chance, that is, *if any such program as the genetic code could develop by **chance?*** As far as we know, program determines the entire metabolism of every kind of life that has ever existed—and program is the *opposite* of chance.

Some scientists today are convinced that the primeval cell was programmed by chance. M. Eigen counts himself as one of these scientists, so that we need to consider in some detail his theories concerning programming of the deoxyribonucleic acid (DNA) molecule and the protein molecules by chance. Our fourth chapter is concerned with such problems and with related difficulties regarding the programming of the DNA molecule.

But prior to this we must investigate a little further to what extent the proteins of life could have been formed by chance—without teleonomy, know-how, and programming.

The Different Types of Proteins

As we have already seen, proteins consist of long chains —and also sometimes of rings—of peptides. The latter consist of amino acids linked by an amide group, as we have already discussed. Proteins originating from living processes consist of l-rotary amino acids which are never formed by chance reactions.

It is important to realize that proteins and also nucleic acids exhibit two types of structure or order.

1. All proteins exhibit one type of order which is purely chemically orientated. This order is of a chemico-physical type. The same sort of order is responsible for the shape of a diamond, as well as the activity of a hormone. It determines the shape and the architecture of a molecule. Proteinoids formed from peptides by chance in a retort exhibit normal molecular architecture, but not the molecular architecture required by the physiology of life. For this reason they do not possess any hormonal or other physiological effectiveness. These proteinoids exhibit chemico-physical order or structure, but not within the architecture required for life. All chemical substances exhibit this first type of chemical order. However if proteins (and other substances) are built by guided, programmed chemical synthesis which is characterized by definite, specific chemical architecture, they can develop such properties as hormonal activity, etc. This activity is dependent on order No. 1.

2. A second, additional type of order appears in certain proteins and in some other substances such as, e.g., nucleic acids. This second type of order always lies strictly within the boundaries of the chemico-physical order No. 1. It represents a higher order which, however, uses the first chemical order as its basis. This second order is a teleonomic, conceptual, often coded order, whereas the first order is, of course, not coded. The second order involves the storing of "project" (system or design), code concept, and teleonomy, so that with its aid machine activity (as of a protein) or information storage (as in a nucleic acid) occurs.

Proteinoids formed in a retort by the usual chemical reactions from amino acids and polypeptides, carry only the first type of order (the purely chemical order of normal valencies) and no second, teleonomic coded order leading to systems and machines and information storage, but which is also chemically anchored.

It is very important to differentiate between the essences of these two types of order, although one kind is dependent on the other. Both types are individual entities. Chemical structure determines the architecture, the form and shape of a molecule, and also determines the form of a crystal or of a diamond. This structure provides the basis of the first type of order. But the same chemical structure can be further developed to provide the second type of order. The chemical order within a protein molecule (the first type of order) can manifest itself in that it, e.g., exhibits pharmacological activity. Certain protein molecules can act in this sense like sweetners: they produce a sweet taste on the tongue (cf Science 181: 6, 7, 73). Others act like insulin: they lower the blood sugar level. Others again can act as antibodies, combining with antigens to protect the body against invaders. Others again act like opiates and have a pain-relieving effect. Such substances are then antagonized by naloxon, just as morphine is so antagonized.

All these pharmacological and physiological activities depend on the first type of order: on the purely chemical architecture of the protein molecule. They fit into certain body receptors where, by an as yet unknown method, their physiological or pharmacological effects are triggered. But this same type of chemical architecture (first order) may be developed to such an extent that it contains a code on which information is transcribed, a sort of chemical writing containing coded information like human writing. So the purely chemical architecture of a molecule (order No. 1) can be developed to such an extent that it corresponds exactly to the shape of a receptor (like a hand fits a glove) to thus induce a physiological or a pharmacological reply. Or the same chemical architecture of a molecule may be so programmed that it becomes "hand writing," not fitting directly into the "glove" of a receptor, to induce a direct effect, but rather storing and relaying "written" coded information or instructions without *directly* inducing a physiological effect. So this second kind of information does not have a direct effect; by means of its coded writing or structure it *instructs* other parts of a cell, thus producing certain physiological, synthetical, or analytical effects. This second kind of order is, so to say, coded, written information, acting indirectly rather than directly by relaying *information* to other parts of the cell, which in turn then produce physiological, synthetical, or analytical effects. This type of order instructs in the same manner as the text of a book. In order to instruct, grammar, code, vocabulary, and syntax are needed. This represents the second type of order.

It is important to realize that the same chemical structure provides the basis of both types of order. Only the first order acts directly (it acts directly on a receptor) whereas the second type of order contains coded information anchored in molecular architecture, which instructs other areas of the cell to act in a certain manner. The borders between the two types of order become indistinct in those places where chemistry "smudges" the code. Although chemistry may smudge the code, it is not capable of producing the information carried by the code. The second type of order is characterized by such terms as "coding," "simulation," and "indirect action."

These somewhat abstract terms are easily explained by the following example: I take a piece of chalk and use it to color the blackboard completely white. So now this blackboard is covered with a thin layer of chalk, which is upheld by a certain chemical architecture (chalk chemistry). The chalk molecules support this layer—they provide the matter, the chemistry, and the order to do so. This type of order is the first order.

If I now take a piece of chalk and with it I write a sentence on the cleaned board, e.g., "the grass is green," then I am also covering part of the board with chalk molecules (chalk chemistry) and that order, just as in the first example. But riding on this first kind of chemical order there appears superimposed on it a second coded order, which contains additional coded, indirect information. The *writing*, "the grass is green," does not look in the least like green grass or taste like green grass; in the presence of sunlight it can neither photosynthesize nor produce oxygen and carbohydrates from carbon dioxide, all of which green grass can do. Rather the writing *symbolizes* green grass in code form. It is a coded description in *chalk molecules* of green grass. The information in the writing "rides" on the chalk molecules and depends on the chemistry of the chalk molecules. Yet the architecture imposed by my writing on the chalk molecules simulates green grass in a secondary mediatory linguistic form, because human language possesses a convention, a code, which the architecture of the sentence "the grass is green" simulates.

A better grasp of this subject-matter is provided by the following illustration: the ink molecules mediating the contents of this book possess their own chemical architecture, rendering the written sentences black, legible, and perceptible. This architecture of the ink molecules exists as a closed system and makes the ink—or the printer's ink—black. Simultaneously, it also provides a basis for the superimposed code-form of a language. *This written form of language is based on the architecture of the printer's ink, without originating from it.* The information contained within the molecules of printer's ink does not in the least provide a basis for the contents, the coded contents of the completed book, although the architecture of ink and the architecture of a sentence or of writing are certainly interdependent. However the chemical constitution of ink is *totally independent* of the coded contents of the text in the book. Information from without has been imposed onto ink chemistry and this information belongs to order of the second kind.

If water is poured onto a text written in ink, this text will thus be modified or partly smudged; but never is fundamentally new information added to the text in this manner. The chemistry of *mutations* in the genetic code information has an effect similar to that of water on our text. Mutations modify or destroy already existing genetic information, but they never create new information. They never create, for example, an entirely new biological organ, such as an eye or ear. Herein lies an error of Neodarwinism, which teaches that fundamentally *new* information is created by mutations.

Neodarwinism teaches additionally that fragments of information can combine to form a complete new text—as if the word "and" could combine with other "and" structures to provide a new concept in a novel. Neither in literary work nor in the text of a genetic code is any new information ever formed in this manner.

The chemical properties of carbon atoms which affect the nature of the DNA molecule, have little to do with the coded contents of the nucleic acids, although both are interdependent—just like the printer's ink and the contents of the text. These two stages may be distinguished from each other in the following manner: The first type of order includes no "projects" or teleonomy, whereas the second type of order (writing) includes coded teleonomy and coded projects. Just as ink and printer's ink do not contain intrinsically any code indicating grass, the first order contains neither a simulated code nor stored information. But the coded writing set down with the aid of printer's ink contains both the first and the second type of order. In the second type, additional information exceeding and transcending that of pure chemistry is included.

Naturally the phenomenon of two superimposed orders

is widespread. A piece of cast iron contains the order harbored by iron. But this order does not suffice to build the order of the cylinder block of a car. The information necessary to build a car's cylinder block is not inherent to iron. However additional "foreign" information for cylinder blocks may be imprinted onto the information harbored by the iron. By taking a car blue print and the iron and combining the two in a workshop, a car cylinder block is formed. The iron itself, however, does not possess the coded information on the blue print, but can receive and carry the same, so that a car cylinder block results. Thus the car cylinder block possesses at the same time the properties of the blue print and also those of the iron molecules. Thus the car cylinder block is a sort of hybrid between the two types of order.

Similarly the chemical components of nucleic acids or of the proteins of life do not possess sufficient information to build an amoeba or a man. But by taking a concept of life (a blue print, so to say) and combining this coded information with the properties of the components of nucleic acids (or of proteins), a man or an amoeba can be formed. However, matter alone—not even the matter from which nucleic acids or proteins are built—does not possess the information of a coded blue print needed to build a man. A living organism is a hybrid between the two types of order.

Autoorganization

For this reason spontaneous biogenesis from dead matter is impossible experimentally and in principle. A source of information for the second type of order is lacking. Thus spontaneous biogenesis never occurs experimentally either—neither today nor in the past. The idea of Eigen and other scientists that a spontaneous *autoorganization* of matter leading up to life can occur is the result of confusion between the two types of order necessary. Many scientists—including Eigen and Monod—hold that the first type of order can spontaneously provide the second type from nothing (by chance). Experiments and information theory contradict this firmly and decisively. Chemical order of the first type does not provide concepts and codes of the second type, for the latter include *codes* which are based on conventions not found in matter intrinsically. The first type neither simulates nor instructs and is therefore not tied to code conventions.

If our natural sciences are to remain scientific, they must remain strictly experiment-orientated. This fact is basic for all experimental thought to such an extent that we must take the risk of repeating the above ideas, for insufficient comprehension of just these facts leads to the misleading opinion that matter plus chance is capable of forming an evolutionary concept (evolution).

It must therefore never be said that chemical order—order No. 1, that is—provides order of the second type (order No. 2): a concept, a code, a car cylinder block, an amoeba, or a human being. The *chalk molecules never provide the concept for a chalk written sentence "the grass is green."* Certainly order No. 2 is based on order No. 1. It is, however, equally certain that order No. 2 is not inherent to or contained in order No. 1. The concept of a car or a typewriter surely does not lie in the chemical and other properties of cast iron (order No. 1), nor are the contents or the concept of a book to be found in the chemical and other properties of paper or printer's ink. The order of the book's contents is imposed from outside onto the paper and the printer's ink, and, thanks to their chemical and other properties, they can retain them. But neither the paper nor the ink employed develop *per se* the contents or the concept of the book. Order No. 1 *never* produces order No. 2, although order No. 1 can carry No. 2.

Several Important Prerequisites And Consequences

These facts bring some radical consequences which we shall now consider. A "cast" of "raw protein" can be made from amino acids—just as cast iron is obtained from molten iron. This "cast" of amino acids (proteinoids), however, never intrinsically possesses the concept for the almost inconceivably complex metabolism of life.

If the cast's basic structure is suitable (the amino acids of which it consists must be laevorotary), the *concept* for this complicated metabolism may be "written" on it in a coded form, just as the information of a book's contents is written on paper. The paper itself does not write the concept of a book, nor do the l- amino acids provide the concept for the metabolism of a living cell. The second type of metabolic information is not inherent in the carbon atom. *Precisely this is one of the main features of the second law of thermodynamics.*

The chemistry of life possesses both types of order—the purely chemical order (order No. 1), as well as the coded, conceptual, written, simulated order (information), which is capable of teleonomically guiding and programming the metabolism of life (order No. 2). Proteins obtained in a retort in the laboratory by condensation of dl- amino acids (or even of optically active amino acids) without coded guidance (such substances are called proteinoids, because their properties differ from those of the proteins of life) possess order No. 1 (chemical order dependent on valency, etc.), but no coded order corresponding to the metabolic concept of life. They are *clean,* unused "paper." Now the evolutionists state that the "paper" itself (the proteins and nucleic acids) produced all the concepts of life from nothing but their own properties by chance. Judging by the evolutionists, the book's "paper" wrote its own contents and its concept—thus the genetic code was allegedly "conceived" by the amino acids themselves, plus chance.

The Preprogramming of Proteins

With this I do not in the least wish to state that the proteins of life—the proteins that have been "written on" —cannot be synthesized within the laboratory. Some have already been synthesized (i.e., "written on"): substances such as insulin have already been artificially produced. However, it is very easily forgotten amid the intoxicating enthusiasm over a successful laboratory synthesis, that natural enzymes were partly employed to carry out these procedures. The enzymes used to tailor these molecules, to transform and transport them, so that the artificial synthesis can be carried out in the laboratory, have usually been procoded by life itself within a cell. Thus life's codes produce in reality the new synthetic molecules, since enzymes precoded by a cell were used for the *in vitro* synthesis. The art of cutting, welding, and transforming organic molecules effected today in the laboratory with the aid of enzymes actually stems from the tools, the enzymes which cut into shape the order of living matter. The protein machines, these enzymes which tailor other molecules, originally owe their wonderful machine-like capabilities to the genetic code of life, which provided them with this teleonomy in the form of a built-in code. The "writing" and the concepts carried by such enzymes are "borrowed" without exception from the concept and the "writing" of some other cell's genetic code. Normally natural enzymes discovered in and extracted from a living cell, or synthetically copied from a natural enzyme, so as to be useful for laboratory chemistry, are employed for the *in vitro* synthesis of artificial life and of its products. With the aid of such concept-carrying molecules amino acids are built up in the laboratory as within a coded living cell, until they are themselves capable of supporting the metabolism of life. Thus artificial life is built up with the aid of enzyme-carried concepts originating from the genetic code of a cell.

It follows from these thoughts that the *"in vitro"* laboratory synthesis of life is also directly or indirectly reliant on the products of biogenesis, for it makes use of the know-how and the teleonomy of certain natural (or copied) enzymes to succeed. Of course, natural enzymes can be synthesized, too, in which case the natural concept of the enzyme is borrowed. Thus artificial laboratory life is also found to be a hybrid of the two types of order, for the enzymes employed in the artificial synthesis had originally been programmed by the codes of life in some cell. Even when a biochemist himself artificially produces all the enzymes required for his synthetic purposes, he has "copied" the conceptual order No. 2 of life into the molecule. His artificial life still remains a hybrid between the two types of order—*and this has nothing to do with chance.* Laboratory synthesis employs know-how and the code of life to pave the synthetic way for laboratory synthesis. The organic molecules are welded, cut, transported, and transformed with the aid of enzyme know-how which is written onto the codes of life (or of the biochemist). Thus the laboratory synthesis of life only proves that man is in the process of learning to use the information stored by the genetic code for his own synthetic purposes— which has nothing in common with chance.

How does this writing on the genetic code and on protein molecules appear? Today nearly everybody is familiar with the nature of the genetic code: four organic bases comprise the four letters of the alphabet of life, which are used in triplet form like the 26 letters of our alphabet. So the chemical structure of the nucleic acid forms the basis of the genetic language. Among the proteins we find a different type of information and language transforming the protein molecules into little super-machines for chemical cutting and welding. This language and this information is anchored in the organic chemistry of the molecule. We must, however, bear in mind that chemistry did not design the languages or their concepts, although both the languages on the DNA and on the protein molecule are based on chemistry. Chemistry did not produce the concepts of the chemical system storing the language. We can refer again to the printer's ink and the contents of a book.

Proposition:
The Paper Writes the Book

As we have already seen, materialistic philosophy of the Neodarwinian type wishes to support the view that the "paper" of life, the amino acid and the nucleic acid does not only possess the inherent information of paper molecules, but that it possesses additionally the inherent information, know-how, and teleonomy sufficient for the entire metabolism of life brought out with the aid of chance and selection. Neodarwinian thought teaches, in fact, that a book's "paper" wrote the book's contents with the aid of chance and selection. It is important to point out that this philosophy rests on no experimental basis, and that the second law of thermodynamics speaks decisively against it. For this reason, science knows nothing of an evolution of the genetic code and its information from the raw materials (the "paper") of life by chance.

A Modern Point of View

Is it true, however, that present-day materialistic biology teaches biogenesis from matter alone—from the "paper molecules"? Certainly this was not so in the past, for a few years ago it was still taught that the chemical reactions of matter are neutral. Chance is also considered "neutral." Evolution was guided solely by natural selection (and perhaps also by species isolation). Thus, in fact, the "paper molecules" themselves are not really considered responsible for evolution.

Lately, this theory was rejected by many. The reasons behind this are logical. All organic chemical reactions are reversible, which means that equilibrium is set up. Chance would require such large quantities of the raw materials of life that all the existing protein molecules on our planet would not suffice to produce a single brain protein molecule by chance. Chance is a method far too wasteful to produce specific optical activity and physiological activity. *A fortiori,* chance alone would suffice even less to produce a code and then its informational contents. We have already discussed these matters. For these and other reasons biogenesis is by some no longer attributed to chance alone. For just this reason Monod's "Monte Carlo hypothesis"[1] on the origin of life and of man was laid *ad acta.*

---

[1] J. Monod, *Le hasard et la necessite,* aux Editions du Seuil Paris, 1970.

It can be shown with the methods available to us today that chance alone cannot achieve what is demanded by modern biology.

As this knowledge has slowly become established under the pressure of progress in information theory and molecular biochemistry, the chance theory had to be questioned. Thus a "knowledge vacuum" developed in some scientific circles. M. Eigen is now attempting to fill this vacuum with his theories. He teaches that chance alone does not, in fact, suffice for biogenesis and evolution, it must be *guided* by the laws of nature. Accordingly, the guidance, i.e. the teleonomy in biology does after all originate from the "paper molecules," i.e., from matter and its governing laws of which biology is constituted. If chance is *guided,* it ceases to be chance. This is axiomatic. Of course Eigen's theory requires this guidance from a source of normal inorganic molecules. Hence teleonomy and concepts are allegedly to be found after all within inorganic molecules, which is, of course, a direct contradiction of the second law of thermodynamics. When left to themselves, inorganic molecules do not tend toward order and teleonomy, but toward disorder and chaos. If "artificial rules of play" are developed to simulate the laws of nature (Eigen), these "rules of play" can in fact act teleonomically, but only because they were expressly developed for this purpose by Eigen and imposed onto matter. However, such "rules of play" do not reflect the real laws of nature regarding teleonomy, for the laws of nature are simply not teleonomical, as Eigen's rules are, and contain none of the concepts required for biogenesis.

The error in Neodarwinian thought lies just in the realm of this problem of concept genesis. The concepts required for the construction of a machine of any sort include: (a) *Knowledge* of the appropriate laws of nature on which the machine is to run—metabolic chemistry for a metabolic machine, combustion chemistry for a combustion machine—and (b) *correct application* of this knowledge. It is obvious that *knowledge* and *application of knowledge represent concepts of thought* which are, however, not inherent in raw matter. The Greeks had a word in their language for the ideas of (a) and (b), namely logos. The laws of matter never in all our experimental knowledge applied themselves to bring forth any machine spontaneously—mechanical or biochemical—for these laws are nonteleonomical.

The Sound Lens in Dolphins

What effects do points (a) and (b) in the previous section have? The so-called "melon" in the dolphin's head[2] provides us with a good example of the importance of concept (a) and (b) in the construction of any specific organ.

Dolphins find their prey with the aid of echo location. They emit a sound, usually of high frequency, the echo of which is then reflected back to the dolphin. In order to locate the position of its prey precisely, the dolphin must concentrate this echo, just as the eye concentrates reflected light to form an exact image of the object reflecting the rays of light. "Sound rays" are concentrated in the dolphin's melon just like light rays in the eye's lens. For this reason one speaks of a "sound lens." The various lipid layers in the melon relay the various wavelengths of the echo in such a manner that they form a clear "sound picture." With the aid of this echo sound picture, the dolphin can locate its prey precisely.

Such a sound lens functions on a concept based on two principles: (a) the speed of sound transmission in various lipids is not constant and (b) the synthesis of the various sound lens lipids exhibiting the differing sound transport velocities. Such a sound lens can hardly have been constructed by means of random experimentation (hit or miss), for the synthetic chemical means of obtaining these various lipids are long and complex. If the wrong lipids had been

---

[2]Usho Uaranais, Henry R. Feldmann, and Donald C. Maltus, "Molecular Basis for Formation of Lipid Sound Lens in Echo Locating Cetaceans," *Nature* 255 (5506): (1975) 340-343.

synthesized, our dolphin could not have survived, because he would have wrongly located his prey. Thus for such a sound lens to be feasible, *prior* knowledge of the various chemical syntheses of various lipids and their respective sound transporting properties is required. Technical know-how is additionally required to work out this knowledge. The synthesis of a sound lens represents a technical feat of a fantastic standard. It is entirely untenable to ascribe such a *technical* feat to chance.

The same, of course, also applies to all other organs, such as the eye, kidney, liver, intestinal tract, and the brain. The hierarchical combination of all these organs into a functioning organism requires even more concepts, and concepts of an even higher order. To attribute this hierarchy to chance and to the laws of nature which are not teleonomic, reveals such incredible credulousness and naiveness that together with G. K. Chesterton we must attribute to Neodarwinians a readiness to believe anything they are told—as long as it is in accord with Neodarwinism! According to Chesterton, this type of credulousness far surpasses all the religious credulousness and superstition on this whole planet.

The concepts behind all biological organs and behind all hierarchical combinations of such organs thus require (a) knowledge of the laws of nature providing the functional basis of the organs and (b) know-how in order to transform such knowledge into practice and to apply it. The laws of nature never execute themselves teleonomically, as we have already seen—the properties of iron in cast iron never act teleonomically and spontaneously to build car cylinder blocks—and carbon, hydrogen, and oxygen atoms never build sound lenses spontaneously either! For this reason we assume that something outside time and matter, called "logos" by the Greeks, fulfilled both functions (a) and (b).

Chapter 4

The Genesis of Biological Information

The Problem of Information Genesis in Archebiopoesis

The theory of evolution teaches that spontaneous chemical evolution of nonliving matter took place before a living cell (the primeval cell, microsphere, or coacervate) could be formed. In other words, nonliving matter experienced spontaneous autoorganization. Manfred Eigen is a leader among scientists advocating this spontaneous autoorganization of inorganic matter.[1] We shall examine his theories first within thermodynamically closed systems and then within thermodynamically open systems.

Thermodynamically Closed Systems

The second law of thermodynamics teaches that within a thermodynamically closed system entropy tends to increase with time. Entropy is a measure of the energy no longer available for useful work, i.e., a measure of order. Energy and order are linked. The above law simply deals with the statistical mean of the energetic situation, so that small, transient deviations from the norm are possible on a molecular basis—that is, small local and transient lowerings of entropy are possible.

---

[1]Manfred Eigen: "Self Organization of Matter and the Evolution of Biological Macromolecules." *Naturwissenschaften* 58 (1971).

An alternative formulation of the second law simply states that within a closed system the total order will tend to decrease. Accordingly, no *overall* spontaneous increase of order could take place in such a system. The total energy available for work within the system will tend to decrease generally and steadily. Obviously, no general progressive autoorganization of matter could take place within a system of this sort. But according to the second law small local exceptions to the rule on a molecular basis are possible.

A closed system of this sort is made up of many molecules, all of which are in a state of dynamic equilibrium, which includes small deviations around an energetic mean. Each spontaneous deviation from the mean in any one direction naturally represents one small improbability or lowering of entropy (i.e., increase of order), which is then compensated by further spontaneous deviations in opposite directions. Eigen maintains that such small deviations (reductions of entropy) can be stored by the replicatory mechanisms of a living cell. Of course, Eigen is here thinking primarily of open thermodynamic systems, but the same principle also applies to closed systems. The main point is that molecular deviations occur around a mean value in both open and closed systems. These deviations represent increased order or lowered entropy, and can, of course, take place either within an open or within a closed system. Now if such spontaneous deviations or lowerings of entropy could be stored and summated, order would constantly and automatically increase or evolve. A localized part of the system (open or closed) would organize itself according to Eigen's scheme.

Thus, we must keep in mind that molecular deviations from the energy mean do take place everywhere within thermodynamically closed systems, as well as in open systems, but that such are local. If such local reduced entropy could be stored, autoorganization of a localized part of the matter within the system would become a reality as Eigen teaches.

But there is a hidden snag in his proposition, as the following question will reveal: Precisely how and when are these small reductions of entropy or increases of order stored? Within a normal, abiotic, closed, thermodynamic system, containing only raw materials, they are, of course, not stored, for the system is in a total state of equilibrium and no living mechanisms are present. Now Eigen suggests that the *replicatory mechanisms of a biological cell could receive and store these small increases of order.* His system will function, then, only if two conditions are taken into account:

1. The energy required to finance the deviations from the order mean must be replaced. Within a closed system this energy would have to be obtained from other parts within the system with the consequence that the total system would become deprived of heat energy spontaneously to finance the locally increased order. Thus the total system would become spontaneously cooler in order to finance the locally increasing autoorganization. We must bear firmly in mind the fact that Eigen not only wishes to explain transformism (origin of new species) by this mechanism, but also biogenesis from nonliving matter, as well— where of course no *biological* storage mechanism for the energy deviations are yet to be found.

2. Eigen teaches an autoorganizaton of matter up to life, i.e., of an autoorganization of raw matter which should permit the formation of life at archebiopoesis, as well as of evolution afterward up to higher species. He employs the replicatory mechanisms of living cells to store the molecular energy deviations, which is, of course, rather problematic, especially *before* biogenesis! Even after life appeared, the information required to finance higher order in higher species is not to be supplied by local molecular energy deviations, as we shall see later, no matter how they might be stored.

It is of greatest importance to note that Eigen's hypothesis requires a *mechanism* to receive and to store the small dynamic energy deviations so as to store reduced entropy locally. Only in this manner could any autoorganization of matter take place— a *mechanism* or a *machine* is absolutely vital to the whole scheme. Without a *storage machine* the entire attempt to rationalize the concept of any autoorganization of matter would fail. Without the aid of a *machine* the second law of thermodynamics forbids categorically any concept of autoorganization. With the aid of an energy consuming machine, the second law allows local reduction of entropy—but not spontaneously! In the *prebiotic* world, however, neither machines nor mechanisms such as those postulated by Eigen existed on principle, for both constitute expressions of teleonomy which is not a property of raw, unorganized matter. Neither teleonomy nor concepts, neither machines, nor projects are represented in matter in its raw, nonhierarchical forms. This is an axiom of physics. According to Jacques Monod, teleonomy (that is, the ability to realize projects or concepts) is a property of life alone (and therefore, in Monod's view, an enigma) and not of unorganized matter. The problem is therefore: Where does Eigen find his *mechanisms* to store the small molecular deviations, so that autoorganization of matter takes place before and up to biogenesis?

As no teleonomic mechanisms or machines existed in prebiotic matter, the vital small deviations could, of course, never be stored. The small increases of order would be immediately ironed out by returning to a state of equilibrium. Without a *receptor mechanism,* they will all be lost immediately. In the prebiotic world, no mechanisms of the type postulated by Eigen existed, so that no autoorganization of matter can have taken place even locally at biogenesis. Accordingly, the autoorganization which we call the chemical evolution of matter leading up to biogenesis is practically and theoretically strictly out of the question. Thus, life cannot have begun spontaneously and ateleonomically as postulated by Eigen and his friends, for the required *mechanisms* or machines were absent. Pasteur's experiments on the spontaneous generation of life—which gave a totally negative result—rest on an excellent theoretical physical basis and Eigen's system for the prebiotic world is, thus, found untenable.

Within a closed thermodynamic system small deviations and the small increases of order are in fact available— energy would be available even with a closed system, provided the total system cooled spontaneously to supply the energy. Wherever deviations occur, a molecular basis for small decreases in entropy exists. Eigen's postulate does not fail due to an insufficient supply of energy within a closed thermodynamic system. As we shall see, the same postulate would also apply within an open abiotic thermodynamic system. *Eigen's entire hypothesis fails solely due to the absence of mechanisms* for storing reduced entropy —and information. This lack of mechanism can be expressed alternatively as follows: all machines and mechanisms represent teleonomic projects nonexistent in a prebiotic world. Thus Eigen's postulate really fails due to lack of teleonomy, machines, project, or concepts up to biogenesis, for raw matter possesses precisely no teleonomy, projects, or machines.

Eigen's ideas would, as we have seen, function very well and matter would organize itself perfectly if he could add teleonomy to his hypotheses in some suitable manner. We are therefore not surprised to learn that he is forced to do just this covertly by postulating the participation of *mechanism* in bringing about autoorganization. We are not, in fact, dealing here with true autoorganization at all, but rather with the organization of matter by means of mechanisms and teleonomy not inherent to matter itself, but inherent in Eigen's self-conceived hypocycles. Thus raw, nonhierarchical matter cannot organize itself, for it does not possess the necessary teleonomy. This fact is inherent in the second law of thermodynamics—which the Neodarwinians regrettably neglect.

The glass beads which Eigen cites in his book *Das Spiel*[2] as an example for the autoorganizing properties of matter, illustrates exactly the same error of logic. The glass beads with which Eigen plays his games do not, in themselves, possess any autoorganizatory capability. Yet with the aid of Eigen's *rules of play*, glass bead patterns (reduced entropy) do develop under the influence of chance. The

---

[2]M. Eigen and Rothild Winkler: *Das Spiel*. R. Piper Verlag (München/Zürich, 1975).

glass beads, representing the atoms and molecules of matter, possess in themselves no teleonomy. Therefore, they do not and cannot organize themselves. The "self-organization" which takes place in Eigen's glass bead games is by no means autoorganization, as Eigen alleges it is, but rather organization by means of carefully conceived teleonomical rules of play residing outside the beads and originating in Eigen's highly teleonomical nervous system! The *teleonomy* of the rules of play is responsible for the order that appears. The teleonomical rules of play are really a teleonomical product of Eigen's metabolism and have nothing to do with any so-called autoorganizational property of matter. Neither glass beads nor matter can in reality organize themselves into patterns. Both are, however, capable of organization by teleonomic rules of play stemming from previously existing teleonomy in the inventor's head.

Thermodynamically Open Systems

The behavior of matter in a thermodynamically open system does not differ much, at least from the point of autoorganization, from that in a closed system. No energy flows into a closed system from the outside. In an open system, such as exists on our planet earth, energy is received in large amounts from the sun, making the earth an open system. In both cases, open and closed, small lowerings of entropy, depending on molecular movements, will occur. The small molecular deviations must in both open and closed systems be retained and stored if autoorganization is to result. Within the closed system the energy for the small deviations comes directly from molecular movement within the system. In an open system, these deviations are augmented by additional energy from outside. At -273 °C all molecular deviations will cease in both open and closed systems. In an open system, more deviations can occur, since energy is continually added to the system from outside. Yet this fact will not alter the final result. The deviations will take place independently of whether the energy is of endogenous or of exogenous origin.

But why go into all this detail? Simply because many scientists are convinced that the simple addition of non-rectified energy to a thermodynamically open system will increase the chances of the autoorganization of matter. In reality, of course, the addition of energy will increase the deviations, the departures from equilibrium, and thus the decreases in entropy, but certainly not their storage by means of a nonexistent mechanism. Thus, the fact emerges that the presence or absence of additional energy is of secondary importance only for the reduction of entropy. The storage of the reduced entropy in a nonhierarchical system of matter is of primary importance. If raw random inorganic matter is irradiated with solar energy, absolutely no autoorganization of matter takes place, as any chemist or physicist knows. However, if a green plant leaf is irradiated with the same amount of solar energy, the energy may be stored as reduced entropy. Sugar and starch are formed, and decreased entropy ("autoorganization") takes place, for chlorophyll is a mechanism, a chemical hierarchical teleonomical machine, suited to storing the harnessed rectified solar energy so that it reduces carbon dioxide (lowering of entropy) to sugars and starch. Without this machine, the added solar energy merely increases the temperature—that is, the deviations but not their storage.

Summarizing: Raw matter within a *closed* system, plus a teleonomic machine, might yield "autoorganization" derived from endogenous energy. Raw matter within an *open* system, plus a teleonomic machine may yield "autoorganization" derived from endogenous and/or exogenous energy. Within both open and closed systems, however, a mechanism (machine, teleonomy, know-how) is essential if any autoorganization is to result. Naturally, such a mechanism can exist in the form of rules of play, for these represent a *simulated machine*, as in Eigen's bead game which yields patterns from random energy.

Present-day Neodarwinians claim that the autoorganization of matter took place prebiotically. They forget, however, to clarify the fact that for all such autoorganization, *mechanisms or machines* are an absolute prerequisite if reduced entropy is to be stored and autoorganization is to result. Such scientists tacitly assume that raw inorganic prebiotic matter was capable of functioning teleonomically as an energy rectifier, such as chlorophyll. This is due to a lack of insight into the principles laid down by the second law of thermodynamics.

The entire theory of evolution stands or falls on two questions which are closely linked with the above considerations:

1. Could raw inorganic matter attain to the necessary autoorganization for biogenesis without the support of a teleonomic storage mechanism for small deviations from chemical equilibrium?—for raw prebiotic matter certainly did not contain any such teleonomical mechanisms. Nonhierarchically organized matter possesses no endogenous teleonomy (mechanisms) and teleonomy is absolutely vital for the genesis of any and all mechanisms. Whether the system involved is open or closed is not particularly important at this stage. The vital point lies in the fact that raw matter never builds teleonomical mechanisms of any sort by itself, therefore, raw matter can never hierarchically organize itself to the hierarchy of life.

2. How could any primeval cell which might have arisen harness its metabolic energy to obtain and store new information in such a way as to convert simple biological species into more complex ones? That is, how could transformism be financed energetically? Neodarwinism requires the new information needed for transformism to have originated by chance. This information is then allegedly sorted out with the aid of selection. An additional section is required to examine this important aspect of Neodarwinism—an aspect which is seldom discussed in evolutionary literature.

The Problem of Transformism and Its Financing With New Information

The purely chemical side of this problem—whether transformism occurred in the past (and whether it still takes place)—will be discussed in succeeding chapters.

Here we would simply like to point out a few other theoretical (and experimental) aspects of transformism.

Rectified or coupled energy must be fed into a system if the total order of the system is to increase. Only coupled energy is capable of financing a real increase in order or a reduction of entropy. But coupled or rectified energy is, of course, exclusively the product of mechanisms or machines (e.g., any internal combustion engine). This fact applies to living as well as nonliving systems, with the main distinction that living systems are programmed endogenously (genetically), so that they can endogenously direct nondirectional energy fed into them, whereas man-made machines are supplied with programs exogenously. In this manner biological replication and growth are financed with the aid of raw energy rectified and coupled by internal programming mechanisms. As far as we can ascertain today, the biological cell possesses no mechanism which could make use of the cell's metabolic energy to generate or finance new genetic *information*. The metabolic energy of the biological cell is utilized for material growth and for replication of the cell and its genetic code. It is not programmed (as may be the case with certain modern computers) for the production of *new programs and of new information*, or for the development of new gene-information using metabolic energy. Precisely because an energy-harnessing system to couple cellular metabolic energy to the generation of new information is lacking, scientists were forced to attribute increased chromosomal information during evolution to chance without any machine controlled energy rectification. It is just this aspect of the Neodarwinian hypothesis which is causing riot today among information theoreticists, for in no other instance do scientists or information theoreticists ascribe growth of information to chance (or to mutation). To attribute the production of new information to chance is to commit a cardinal heresy in the world of modern information.

But a still more serious heresy is committed when one not only attributes the formation of new information to chance, but in addition ascribes the information storage and retrieval mechanisms of the same also to chance. Chance develops no new information, and it certainly does not form information storage or retrieval systems. Chance can always modify existing information, but it can never provide basically novel concepts or new information.

Entropy and Information

The majority of Neodarwinians today believe that the problem of biological information production is automatically solved by simply elucidating the problem of decreased entropy. Eigen's proposed reductions of entropy[3] which are supposedly subsequently trapped by a hypothetical genetic replicatory mechanism tend in this direction. The production of small decreases of entropy is interpreted as though they brought with them automatically a generation of information. The real problem of information generation is, as it were, swept under the carpet. Can it really be maintained that deviation from the energy mean molecularly is identical with information generation? This point is important, for on it depends a substantial part of the Neodarwinian hypothesis of spontaneous biogenesis and transformism. For it is claimed that genetic information automatically originates when the small entropy reductions of molecular deviations from the mean are retained. Does this point of view correspond in fact to modern information theory? *If not, then the entire basis for Neodarwinian explanation of biogenetic information production is no longer scientifically tenable.*

The real question is, therefore: Can the existence of small entropy decreases as a result of molecular deviations really be equated with the generation of new, even though transient, information? We propose to employ the following experiment in order to examine this question. We shall use an experiment with cards bearing only two printed symbols—the dots and dashes of Morse code—for this

---

[3] *cf* Eigen and Winkler (footnote 2).

purpose. According to the laws of probability, we shall obtain sooner or later by chance procedures the following dot-dash sequence (· · · - - - · · ·) assuming always that these randomly produced patterns of Morse letters are retained or stored. This particular sequence represents a system of somewhat decreased entropy. If we show this system of dots and dashes to a ship's radio officer, he immediately not only sees reduced entropy, that is, the unusual sequence, but he also sees something more in it, namely a ship in distress. The sequence is thus not only that of reduced entropy. It is also a coded message. Information has been relayed by its means to the officer over and above that of mere reduced entropy. If we show the identical system of dots and dashes to a bushman, he will only see the improbable pattern, so to speak, the decreased entropy. Obviously the officer obtains a message, that is, information from the system which the bushman neither sees nor understands. *Since the officer is familiar with the Morse code convention,* he can extract the hidden information from the reduced entropy which the bushman cannot. The officer knows that at least two parties had mutually agreed to a Morse code convention which introduces certain information into previously adopted systems of dots and dashes (reduced entropy) so that messages (information) can be stored by a system of this sort.

Decreased entropy systems are valuable for the transmission of information because they are improbable—they will not appear everywhere spontaneously. For this reason information and codes may be *inserted* into them. By using this improbable system, there is little danger that it will appear anywhere by chance and thus randomly simulate "information" which really does not exist. Only such decreased entropy patterns may be employed which do not arise of their own accord, otherwise they would simulate nonexistent messages. With increasing complexness of the message, a corresponding decrease in the entropy relaying or bearing the information is required. It is of great importance to realize that the conceived dot-dash system in itself, its reduced entropy, has no connection whatsoever with the genuine information it carries—that is, in this case, with the emergency.

If a random selection of the letters of the alphabet is undertaken by means of dice, the following reduced entropy system could be obtained after a certain time and a certain number of throwings: *Grandmother is dead.* It has become a settled convention of the English language to insert the information of Grandmother's decease on to this particular sequence of letters. The letter sequence itself does not however, resemble Grandmother's death at all, and the system yielded by means of the dice has nothing to do with her actual death, that is, with the genuine information on her death.

The information is introduceable into any system of decreased entropy or increased improbability: however, the decreased entropy, the improbability itself is not information. Thus information *per se* cannot be equated to improbability even though information is improbable! We transmit information and messages by inserting it onto the systems of lowered entropy we call languages and codes for purely practical reasons. However, the message itself is not to be equated to the lowered entropy. For this reason, it is nonsense to claim, as the Neodarwinians sometimes do (*cf* Eigen, *das Spiel),* that the production of small entropy decreases represents the same phenomenon as the production of information. It is for just this reason that I firmly reject the postulate that random molecular deviations produce information if they are summated and stored. The Neodarwinian claim represents a striking abuse of the information theory of Norbert Wiener and Shannon, which latter teaches that information and concepts are inserted by entirely human conventions onto reduced entropy systems, but that the reduced entropy system is by no means to be equated with the information borne by it.

In this context it is taught that the improbable sequences of the four DNA nucleotides of the genetic code comprise in themselves the actual information of the genetic code, that is, the instructions for building organs such as the eye or the kidney. The DNA nucleotides *carry* this information, but they do not constitute it. Judging by Eigen's

Neodarwinian thought, the *information* for building the cell and the organism, the organs, nerves, and the brain arose entirely from molecular deviations that were retained by some mechanism formed by chance. Such deviations are supposed to have provided the information to wire a brain capable of initiating and controlling speech. Technically educated persons know, of course, that complex information does not consist merely of molecular deviations, but is an entity which may ride on such reduced entropy. Neodarwinians explain the origin of the technical information necessary for wiring a brain as a mere sum of small molecular deviations. In reality, such reduced entropy deviations support and store information, but do not manufacture it, nor can it be equated to them. Teleonomy is the information source, for raw matter does not contain such teleonomy or concept. We know that all information and all messages stem from a source of intelligence or a concept of some sort. This information is then transmitted by means of attaching it with the help of conventions to some arbitrary reduced entropy system.

Thus Neodarwinian thought requires basically the prebiotic autoorganization of raw matter (which the second law categorically excludes), the creation of information by random deviations (which information theory categorically forbids), the encoding of information by chance (without the help of exogenous code conventions), the storage of information by chance and its retrieval also by chance. The Darwinian hypothesis sets out to explain the origin and the replication of a biological organism (a super machine), immensely more complex than a modern automobile, by means of random deviations. If we were to accept such an hypothesis, we would have to be willing in principle to accept the origin and the development of any other teleonomic machines solely and exclusively by means of the molecular deviations of iron molecules and by selection on the car market in the game of supply and demand, but without the aid of any teleonomic construction mechanisms, blue prints, or concepts.

According to this scheme, competition plus chance would suffice to explain the development and origin of all cars. Thus engineers, machines, and workshops would no longer be required to produce cars. In principle this would be equivalent to the Darwinian doctrine that deviations from the norm (mutations) and natural selection, that is, competition within biology alone, suffice to explain the origin and the development of all the known biological super machines or cellular organisms. The role of plan, teleonomy, and know-how is excluded by this scheme, even in organisms of far greater complexity than cars. Random, endogenously generated molecular deviations sorted out by means of teleonomic rectification (i.e., by means of a mechanism) are, of course, not the real causes behind any hierarchic machines and are, therefore, not behind biological organisms. Only random exogenously induced deviations suffice to express teleonomy which may then be sorted out by selection in competition. Neodarwinian thought, because it has not recognized the difference between exogenously and endogenously induced molecular deviations, is not capable of explaining the cause of teleonomic rectification in matter which is not inherent in matter itself.

Chapter 5

Programmed By Chance?

Chance as a Programming Agent

In the past Darwinians held the opinion that biogenesis could be accounted for by the chance formation of amino acids and their subsequent condensation to more complex products. Darwin and his friends, of course, knew nothing of the internal coded programming of a cell, and thus were free to assume that the entire primeval cell was originally the result of chance chemistry.

Today, however, the situation has been entirely changed by advancing knowledge. We now know that the chemical and physiological metabolic cycle of a cell—and of life in general—is never left to chance. All chemical and other processes within a cell are strictly preprogrammed, even though chance supplies the basic chemical movement behind the programmed metabolism. All synthesis and all catabolism in all cells is determined and regulated by a coded program, although the purely chemical reactions carrying out programmed metabolism are subject to the influence that chance exercises in all molecular and atomic movement. The program is located in the cell nucleus on the DNA molecules and is written in code form—that is, in principle as in a book, although naturally neither paper nor the 26 letters of our alphabet code are employed. To store and retrieve the information contained in the nucleus, the cell possesses its own language, its own code, its own grammar, and its own storage medium ("paper"). The letters themselves consist of four bases and are used as triplets. The "paper" consists of phosphate and deoxyribose chains for DNA. The language or code and the letters of this code are identical for all living organisms

(plants, viruses, animals, and humans.)

The origin of this biological language must be sought in a chemical *concept* regulating all cell processes by means of code and grammar and not in mere aconceptual chemical reactions. Identification of this chemical concept's origin would, of course, greatly contribute to a better comprehension of the meaning of life itself. An increasing number of scientists, especially those of materialistic convictions, are today attempting to discover a rational material explanation of the origin of the concept, the code, and the language of life. Thus, since concept, code, and genetic language are the prerequisites for the programming of life, we must look for their origin within the laws of information theory, which excludes those of mere chance, naturally occurring, inorganic chemical reactions.

In everyday language the terms "concept," "code," and "program" are linked with such terms as "intelligence," "thought," "conception," or "information." Terms such as those of "concept," "thought," "information," and "intelligence" are connected with the old fashioned words "logos," "sense," and "mind." So it would seem that the discovery of a concept or of a language code or of any system or machine mechanism for the storage and reproduction of information in living cells would automatically demand the existence of a concept, code, "logos," mind, or intelligence behind the cell's origin, that is, behind biogenesis, for codes can arise only from concepts. Since, however, materialistic philosophy does not permit us to see concepts such as "mind" or nonmaterial intelligence behind the origin of material life, it automatically became necessary to search for the source of language, code, mind, and information in biological cells exclusively within matter and the laws of chance.

However, it is just this task which has turned up so many major difficulties. For we know that matter itself is not teleonomical, it possesses no concepts, no teleonomic biological codes, no "projects," and no forward-looking plans, i.e., it exhibits in its raw primeval forms neither intelligence nor "mind." Yet the living cell is really just a bag full of projects, of teleonomy, and of concepts, and, therefore, of mind. The materialist is forced to seek the origins of this programming and of these concepts of life in "nonmind," i.e. in matter and chance, because he believes that matter and time represent the total reality of this universe. A considerable amount of "mental acrobatics" is required to obtain programs magically, to conjure up projects and concepts out of "nonmind," "nonprojects," and "nonprograms," i.e. out of matter and chance. It is just these mental acrobatics which are carried out to support materialism that we need to consider more closely, for they are the basis of much that is offered to our youngsters in our secondary and high schools and taught in universities as the sole scientific explanation of life and its codes.

If a reasonable materialistic view of biogenesis is to be taught as a fact, the problem of programming, simulation, language, code, and translation of a code—obtained spontaneously from noncode—must be squarely faced. For matter, which is known to possess neither plans, intelligence, nor programming, is alleged by the materialists to have conjured them all up like a rabbit out of a hat. The cell can in fact "take decisions," it contains many chemical concepts and information-related programs. The entire metabolism of a cell proves this. However, inorganic matter can take no such decisions at all—such as those necessary to produce optical resolutions of amino acids. Thus the problem confronting us boils down to this one point: How does a cell spontaneously develop from inorganic matter the "power of decision," concepts, teleonomy, and programs from inorganic matter which does *not* possess *any* of these? The generation of teleonomy from nonteleonomy is the great problem among thoughtful materialists. Monod called it "an enigma." We shall now consider it more closely.

The Nature of the Cell's Program

All biological cells are guided by program stored in the cell nucleus on DNA molecules in code form. Just as a factory drill is guided by programmed punched strips, all cellular syntheses and catabolic processes are teleonomically remotely controlled by the coded program in the nucleus. Little is left to chance within a cell. The entire chemical metabolism is preprogrammed by code. A cell's reactions to its environment are also to a large extent preprogrammed.

Before we can discuss the origin and the function of a coded teleonomic system of this type, the system itself as it functions today must be at least partly understood. In order to avoid the lengthy explanations necessary to clarify such a system theoretically, we shall describe the major traits of the genetic code system with the aid of several simple analogies.

The internationally recognized distress call is "S O S." This call contains information within a coded phrase, which may also be expressed as: · · · - - - · · · The dots and dashes represent the two letters of Morse code. · · · is equivalent to our letter "S" and - - - to our "O." We can store or transmit the Morse alphabet in various manners. For example, the letters can be retained on paper, written on a birthday cake with cake icing, or an airplane could write the same letters in the sky with smoke from a smoke cartridge. The message and the information remain the same, namely "S O S" in whatever medium they are transmitted or stored. The dots and dashes of the Morse code might even be knotted on a string, the dash being represented as a larger knot and the dot as a smaller knot. (See Fig. 2.)

In this last case no paper surface is required to relay the message contained in the Morse code, the dimension of only a simple piece of string will suffice. By means of a system of this type, a string carrying single knots and and double knots (= dashes) could be used to "write" and to store Goethe's "Faust." The ancient Incas used similar systems of strings and knots to record their ancestry, history, and business transactions. They possessed neither paper nor ink, but were by no means illiterate. They "wrote" by means of knots and a string code instead of using our 26 letters written on paper. Such an Inca system can either be read with the eyes (as we read letters on paper) or with the sense of touch—by feeling the knots as they slip through the fingers. Thus this system is a script

Figure 2. String or cord with knotted SOS message in Morse Code. Three smaller knots represent the Morse Code dots = "S" and the three bigger knots represent the Morse Code dashes = "O".

capable of being read by sight or by the sense of touch—just as Braille is read by a sense of touch.

The information for programming all biological cells is stored by means of a similar system and is read by contact with ribosomes. Four chemical letters are fastened onto two strands. The two strands constitute the so-called "double helix" for they occur in the form of a spiral. Instead of consisting of two letters such as the dots and dashes of the Morse code, the cell code system consists of four letters in the form of simple chemical bases (A, T, G, and C in DNA, A, U, G, and C in ribonucleic acid = RNA). A = Adenine, T = Thymine, G = Guanine, C = Cytosine, and U = Uracil. As already mentioned, the biological strands differ from the Inca string system in consisting of a *double* helix. The four chemical letters lie between the double helix like the knots between a double string. Sugar molecules (ribose or deoxyribose) bind the chemical letters (A, T, G, and C in DNA; A, U, G, and C in RNA), and phosphate molecules bind the sugar molecules together into a long double strand. Schematically the system may be represented as shown in Fig. 3.

This double helix system carrying four chemical letters permits the retention of information just as the Inca system does on a string or the 26 letters of our alphabet permit the retention of a poem on paper. In principle, the sequences of the four bases carry their information just as the order of the dots and dashes of the Morse code carries its information. In technical language the sequences of the four bases function just like the various sequences of the 26 letters of our alphabet. By means of a double helix system of four letters, entire books filled with information could be written by merely altering the sequences—just as we write books by varying the sequences of the letters of our alphabet. In this manner the double helix system within a human sperm and a human egg contains the total coded building instructions for synthesizing the complete human being. On paper using our alphabet system, this human genetic information on one human zygote would fill over 1,000 volumes each of 500 pages—a total of 500,000 printed pages. That is, one human egg the size of a pinhead holds 500,000 printed pages' worth of information and chemical instructions. The egg—and the cell in general—is a masterpiece of miniaturized information storage and retrieval. One such zygote contains the entire information and instructions required to build an entire human being—and also that required to synthesize all his offspring!

Having set out the above well known information, the following questions confront us: (1) How can we envisage the origin in the past of *such a code system in itself?* (2) How can we envisage the origin of the *contents* of such a system—i.e., of the information and the chemical instructions carried by this system? The situation could be elucidated alternatively by posing the following two questions: (1) How did the system which we call a gramo-

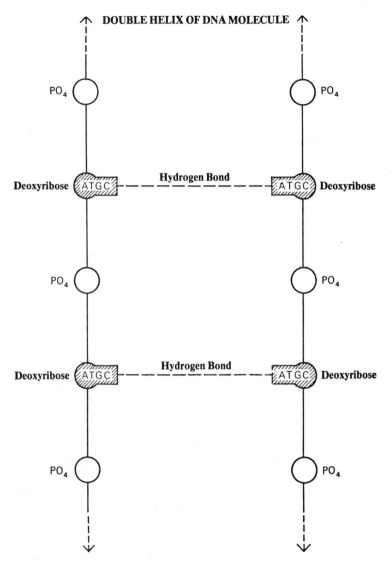

Figure 3. Deoxyribonucleic acid (DNA) molecule (schematic section of the double helix). The four letters of the cell alphabet are made up of four bases: A T G C (A = adenine, T = Thymine, G = Guanine, C = Cytosine) in DNA, A U G C (U = Uracil) in RNA. These four bases are bound by sugar molecules (ribose and deoxyribose); the sugar molecules themselves are bound by phosphate molecules (PO_4), so that they form the two long chains of the double helix. Hydrogen bonds between the base molecules form bridge-like links between the two chains.

phone or phonograph originate? and (2) How did the information (music, poems, etc.) stored within the gramophone or phonograph system originate? In this case, the *gramophone system* would be comparable to the DNA molecule, while information (music, etc.) contained by the system is equivalent to the information (instructions for synthesis, etc.) carried by the DNA molecule. Both problems are of equal importance, for they will illuminate the actual nature and significance of man and biology.

How does the materialistic scientist and the evolutionist explain archebiopoesis (the primeval development of life, biogenesis) and the genesis of such a code system? An explanation for the formation of the genetic machinery (the "gramophone" system) and an explanation for the origin of the contents of this machinery (the "music" on the "records") are thus in question.

The genetic machinery possesses a mechanism for the translation and realization of the language it bears, and this also must be explained biogenetically. Any such explanation precludes, if it is to be considered as reasonable by scientific materialists, the involvement of prebiotic intelligence. Materialism obliges one to settle exclusively for explanations involving nonintelligent (chance) origins. Thus the laws and rules òf inorganic matter must if the materialistic view is correct, provide both the system (i.e., the gramophone "mechanism"), as well as the information (concepts, "record contents") the mechanism bears. Both the mechanism and the information it stores must be accounted for without resorting to the help of intelligence of any sort. Programs, translation mechanisms, and the realization in chemistry of a simulated system, together with the information and instructions it bears must be obtained exclusively from the laws of inorganic matter only.

The major difficulty in arriving at an adequate hypothesis within the tenets of scientific materialism lies in the following fact: inorganic matter is known to possess no biological teleonomy, no biological programs, no biological concepts, no simulated language codes, no replicatory systems, no teleonomic machinery, and no biological plans. Nevertheless, if the tenets of scientific materialism are correct, inorganic matter must provide, before life can appear, just this machinery, precisely such systems, and the whole teleonomy of life (information, metabolic concepts, etc.). Teleonomy must develop out of non-teleonomy spontaneously, which is, as Monod so pithily admitted, nothing but an enigma and as such not very promising scientifically.

Manfred Eigen's Glass Beads

Manfred Eigen deals with just this problem of the supposedly spontaneous generation of life from nonlife, of plan and of teleonomy from nonplan and from non-teleonomy. He states that chance, guided by nature's rules of play, has accomplished precisely this master-piece (biogenesis), that is, the spontaneous formation of biological order from inorganic order. To achieve this end Eigen proceeds to describe various games depending on chance which, under certain rules of play, will produce order out of nonorder. He attempts to prove his view with the aid of his various bead games.[1]

To do this, Eigen declares that the properties of matter and the laws of nature which are inherent in inorganic matter act upon chance so as to guide it *teleonomically*—in spite of the fact that the properties of inorganic matter are biologically nonteleonomic. Thus is formed, according to Eigen, the teleonomic material apparatus necessary for the appearance of physical life (the metabolic machine). He and his colleagues all agree that no extramaterial guidance (such as an act of creation by God) or intelligence is necessary to explain the teleonomic order of the biological cell. Eigen and the majority of materialistic scientists maintain that the immanent proper-

---

[1] *cf* M. Eigen and Rothild Winkler: *Das Spiel.* Naturgesetze steuern den Zufall. R. Piper Verlag (Munchen/Zurich, 1975) p. 404.

ties of inorganic matter independently produced the programs, the codes, the systems, and the informational
contents of the DNA molecule.   That is, everything
written in the genetic "book" stems exclusively from
inorganic matter guided by the inherent laws of matter.

As we have already mentioned, an attempt is thus being
made to derive the conceptual contents of a book from
the properties of the *material paper* on which the text
of the book is written, which amounts to maintaining that
the paper on which the Bible is written wrote the contents
of the Bible.   The paper, together with nature's rules of
play (the laws of nature in the paper) is held to be responsible for developing the book (the system), as well
as its contents (code, concepts, and information).   Chance
plus the rules of play inherent in the "paper" are thought
to have acted upon the paper so as to spontaneously and
independently produce both the system (the book) and its
conceptual contents (the text).

We can express the above thought with even greater
clarity and must do this in order to demonstrate the intellectual suicide to which the materialistic approach to
biogenesis is rapidly leading us: Before us lies a copy of
a book containing Shakespeare's Hamlet.   The entire contents of this book, as well as its print, binding, chapter
headings, and plotted intrigues are postulated to have
developed—to retain our analogy—solely and totally out
of the paper, i.e., out of the matter comprising the book
and out of the rules of play governing the properties of
the paper, i.e. out of the laws of nature acting upon the
paper.   Thus materialistic philosophy and therefore also
materialistic science demands that the "paper" (the matter) upon which biological life is built, produced the
entire cell as well as its systems, codes, and contents,
its "chapters," "plots," and metabolic cycles.   Random
molecular movements within matter together with the rules
of play governing the properties of matter are alleged to
have created the entire "book" of life.   According to these
views, programs or teleonomy outside matter had nothing
whatever to do with archebiopoesis (the "publication of
the book").   The scientific materialist often believes,

if he is consistent to his materialism, that nothing whatsoever exists outside the dimensions of time and space.
For this reason matter alone (the "paper") must be the
exclusive inventor, author, and supporter of all the programs, concepts, and the teleonomy of life. Put briefly,
all biological teleonomy must be inherent in matter—although according to the second law of thermodynamics,
matter possesses no such teleonomy leading spontaneously
to decreased entropy or programs.

The Nature of Language

Manfred Eigen makes the most recent attempt to discover a method of attributing to the "paper" of the book
the responsibility for the generation of its contents—in this
case the genetic code and its information. He sets out to
prove his hypothesis by means of various glass bead games.
The burden of his message lies in the fact that chance
acting within certain rules of play inherent to matter does
develop patterns or order, that is, reduced entropy. Hence
he deduces that information and codes, just like order and
patterns, can develop directly out of pure chance acted
on by certain rules which he compares to the laws of
nature. If the formation of order and patterns in glass
beads by means of rules and chance is possible, then,
argues Eigen, the same phenomenon (that is the formation
of the order and patterns of codes and information) must
be possible on the same basis in molecular chemistry.
Thus he "proves" that the genetic code and biogenesis
could well have been developed by chance with the help of
the rules of play provided by the laws of nature.

We shall now consider a few simplified examples to
clarify Eigen's views. They are not always the same examples as those used by him, but they illustrate the same
principles.[2]

By disturbing a reaction in equilibrium it is possible to

---

[2] *cf* Eigen's original examples (see Footnote No. 1).

temporarily increase order, i.e. to reduce entropy. This reduction of entropy can easily be induced by a chance happening. If any such disturbed reaction equilibrium or deviation could be retained by suitable mechanisms within the system, the increased order could be stored and summated. It would no longer be only temporary. Eigen then assumes that this retained increased order or reduced entropy resembles the order of the genetic code itself. If order can be spontaneously generated in this manner why should the order of programs, of codes, and of information not be generated by means of the same chance reactions and rules of play without the assistance of any exogenous "mind" or intelligence of any sort? Teleonomy and programs of this type are thus alleged to have been obtained by retaining mere disturbances of chemical equilibrium reactions. In this manner life is supposed to have been generated without the aid of any exogeneous intelligence. These are the rules of play behind Eigen's thoughts on archebiopoesis.

Alternatively, the above thoughts may be formulated in the following way: We take a hat filled with many sets of cards, each carrying one of the letters in the alphabet A to Z. Let us assume that the first card drawn from the hat bears the letter "A." The same card drawing procedure is continued according to the same rules of play. A second time we obtain a card bearing the letter "N." A third choice provides us with the letter "D."

In this manner we have by means of purely random selection, within certain rules of play, obtained the sequence "AND" without the aid of any intelligent teleonomy. A sequence ("AND") representing lowered entropy—for it is a pattern representing increased order—has been obtained by chance. By continuing this same game, an entire sentence could be obtained in precisely the same manner: e.g., "I LOVE YOU." It would, however, be necessary to make random selections very often and according to very definite rules to obtain this end. This method could be accelerated by appropriate new rules of play. By similar but even more appropriate proceedings, Goethe's "Röslein, Röslein, Röslein rot,

Röslein auf der Heide" could certainly be obtained. Random selection and rules of play are the only prerequisites (apart from matter in the form of the cards and energy) required for such accomplishments, even if the results are highly improbable, wasteful of energy, as well as time consuming.

As we have already seen, the genetic code consists of a double helix (double strand) on which sentences, information, instructions, and programs are written with the aid of four letters in coded sequences. The conclusion of the scientific materialists is that words and indeed sentences can be formed by chance from our 26 letters and therefore also by the four chemical letters of the genetic code.

Eigen's postulate for the origin of life and of the genetic code is therefore as follows: If meaningful sequences such as "AND" and "I LOVE YOU" can be formed by chance and rules of play and without a real author, and if such randomly formed sequences carry information, as our word "AND" and the sentence "I LOVE YOU" carry information, then reduced entropy, information, and code have developed from chance and rules of play, as he postulated. Accordingly, programming and information generation on a molecular basis can take place in the same manner. Thus intelligence and authors are not a prerequisite for the development of the reduced entropy, the codes and the information of life. Chance and rules of play alone will suffice. Eigen concludes on this basis, that an act of creation by an intelligent Author or Creator need no longer be postulated in order to explain the origin, the programming, and the coding of the genetic system. A higher, intelligent being behind the creation which we call biology is, therefore, superfluous, according to this school of thought.

Summarizing the above: The modern scientific materialist believes with the Neodarwinians that the formation of biological, chemical, and coded combinations carrying information can be explained by rules of play and chance. Allegedly no teleonomy or intelligence is required. Since life consists of chemical combinations and coded programs, archebiopoesis has supposedly been adequately explained by chance and rules of play without any intelligent exogenous interventions by an Author or Creator.

Are these postulates tenable from the point of view of current science, including the sciences of chemistry and information theory? As we have already seen, the organic chemistry postulated by many Neodarwinians to explain the formation of the proteins of life is often unfounded. For, in the first place, the important problem of the origin of the optical activity of biological substances has not been solved. In the second place, the problem of the reversibility of organic reactions has not been solved either. It is now necessary to examine on a purely scientific basis Eigen's postulate of the chance development of biological mechanisms, information, and genetic programs.

In order to do this, we shall have to repeat the experiment described above which delivered "AND" and "I LOVE YOU" by random selection and rules of play. This time we shall introduce a small alteration into the experimental "reaction conditions." I shall conduct exactly the same experiment previously described, but in German-speaking Switzerland instead of in England. With the aid of chance and defined rules of play, I obtain the sequence "AND" (highly unlikely, of course), just as I did the first time in England. I am very pleased and congratulate myself in front of the Swiss audience for having again generated information and a meaningful coded word by chance without the aid of an author. Triumphantly I display the word "AND" on the cards to the astonished Swiss. But for some reason they look at me quite uncomprehendingly. I call out to them in German that my experiment has succeeded and I show them again the allegedly meaningful word "AND" produced by chance. Then a polite old Swiss gentleman rises and points out to me in his best German that, even if the sequence "AND" is meaningful to myself and my English-speaking colleagues, it still means *nothing whatsoever* to him and the German-speaking audience. The Swiss are not familiar with the word "AND." For them the sequence is, therefore, entirely meaningless. For them the sequence "AND"

does certainly signify increased order and therefore reduced entropy, for it is improbable and patterned. But
for a Swiss person speaking no English, it contains *no
linguistic coded information, i.e. no message.* For my
Swiss audience for some unlikely reason did not speak a
word of English!

Language Conventions

Certainly "AND" is an example of increased improbability and therefore of reduced entropy and increased
order. Surely "AND," therefore, represents the creation
of order? Certainly it represents reduced entropy and,
therefore, the creation of new order, but it does not necessarily in itself bear information. In order to transmit
meaning, improbable sequences of symbols of some sort
exhibiting reduced entropy, such as "AND" are chosen.
Then by *language conventions* these improbable sequences
exhibiting reduced entropy are charged with meaning,
conceptual contents or with *information* and *messages.*
Any sequences of symbols exhibiting reduced entropy or
increased order can be taken and charged with meaning,
messages, or information according to any language convention. Likewise the sequence of symbols (reduced
entropy) · · · · · · · · has been charged with meaning
(information) according to a code convention. The basis
of a code is totally arbitrary from the point of view of
the actual *symbols employed* (but not from the point of
view of language rules). Any system of reduced entropy
(of symbol sequences), even though it is in itself totally
void of information can be used for language and code.
A language convention which is quite arbitrary is established and simply lays down that a particular system of
symbols or patterns bears a certain definite meaning.
Thus the *meaning* (information) of a sequence is *not
inherent* to the sequence—the meaning of "AND" does
not necessarily and automatically reside within this system of reduced entropy. Language conventions external to

the letters of the alphabet have determined the meaning and the information of the sequence "AND" which thus possesses in itself *no intrinsic meaning or information.* Language convention which is entirely exogenous to any sequences has decided that "AND" in English is a conjunction with the same meaning as "ET" in French or "UND" in German or "OG" in Norwegian. *Human convention*—not the "AND" in itself—produces meaning or information and injects message into the sequence "AND." "AND" itself as a sequence showing reduced entropy is completely meaningless—even though it inherently represents a reduction of entropy and therefore a creation. Thus, if "AND" is formed by chance, the *present meaning* of "AND" is by no means produced by chance at the same time. The *information* borne by "AND" is produced *exclusively* by the appropriate language convention which has nothing whatever to do with the reduced entropy sequence or its generation by chance. The language convention alone of all English speaking people to the effect that "AND" bears the same meaning as the mathematical "+" sign or the "∧" sign endows the sequence "AND" with meaning and information. If we show the sequence "AND" to a Japanese, a Turk, or a Chinese, they will all stare at us quite uncomprehendingly for it means just nothing to them (unless they have learned English language conventions) for they know nothing of the "AND" language convention, which alone confers meaning onto this particular sequence.

This fact (the meaning of language convention in information generation and transmission) is of such vital importance that it must be further established. Let us assume that we are once again playing with our cards according to the same rules. This time we randomly obtain the sequence "OG," which would be relatively easy to obtain by chance for it is of low entropy reduction. Regrettably the *meaning* of the sequence "OG" is only known to those familiar with the Scandinavian languages (OG—Scandinavian for AND). For an Englishman, American, Japanese, or Turk, "OG" carries neither meaning nor information. Every Turk, Japanese, American, or Englishman with sufficient scientific education will recognize that the sequence "OG" represents a case of somewhat reduced entropy or increased order. However a *Norwegian* when he hears or sees "OG" recognizes not only the *reduced entropy,* but additionally he sees the *information* and the *meaning* carried by "OG."

The information relayed by the symbols of a written language is certainly linked to reduced entropy according to the tenets of modern information theory, but it represents *more* than simply reduced entropy. Symbols representing reduced entropy are selected arbitrarily for code purposes and language information is certainly associated with these symbols (decreased entropy), for we could transmit no information without the "attachment" of information by a language convention to increased order sequences. But these order sequences only *bear* information. They do not constitute information.

Thus a linguistic symbol (a sequence of letters) only carries the meaning and information lent to the letters by a source of information according to the rules of a *language convention.* Convention does affect all translations of the symbols involved. Exogenous information is introduced onto the symbol only by language convention. We must again emphasize that neither meaning nor information lie within the sequence itself, as it is just this point that Eigen entirely misses. Information and meaning are introduced onto the symbols. The symbols themselves can certainly be produced by chance, but the meaning and information they may bear is not produced by chance at the same time. Meaning is an antithesis to chance and is, therefore, not produced by chance.

The reason why reduced entropy and order of the type we have discussed can be created apparently by chance, whereas information, concept, and instructions cannot, is highly interesting and not generally known. It is as follows: When a reduced entropy sequence such as "AND" is produced on a transmission medium such as paper, it is produced irreversibly, that is, with *covert decision making,* as we have shown in the monkey and typewriter experiments cited by Huxley in the Wilberforce debate.[3]   This is possible because such sequences are committed to paper once and for all and do not return through the typewriter keys to the monkey's brain reversibly.   It is this hidden decision making which does the creating and not chance.   Information, instructions, and programs are, on the contrary, concepts, which are only held to sequences on paper by conventions which can be altered and reversed at will by those who decide on conventions.   They are not produced once and for all as a sequence is on paper, so that *no hidden decision making* is involved when pure concepts or information are conceived. For this reason reduced entropy sequences arise by *apparent* chance, but not true information, concepts, or programs as such.

Thus our "AND" and our "OG," produced by "chance" never obtained their meaning and their information by chance.   Chance never created meaning, language, information, and projects.   Chance coupled with covert decision making merely produced the reduced entropy, but not the information borne by the reduced entropy. By chance the "AND" and the "OG" sequences corresponded to those sequences carrying a certain meaning in the (conventional) use of the English or the Scandinavian language and they, therefore, at first appeared to an Englishman or a Scandinavian to carry information and meaning "in themselves."   However, it remains a cardinal error in logical thought to claim—as do Manfred Eigen and others—that meaning, information, projects, and language develop by chance, because "AND," "OG," and other reduced entropy sequences are formed by chance (and decision making, which is, of course, never mentioned).   Here we have a typical example of superficial scientific materialistic thought.   Language conventions

---

[3]A. E. Wilder Smith, *Man's Origin, Man's Destiny,* Harold Shaw Publishers, Wheaton, Ill., 1968, p. 63, *cf.* CLP Publishers, San Diego, CA 92115.

have provided "AND" and "OG" with meaning, but
without language convention "AND" and "OG" are mere
reduced entropy sequences void of information, instructions, codes, or language. Chance, together with decision
making, produces sequences of reduced entropy, which are
however, meaningless unless with the help of language
conventions meaning is imposed from without onto them.
Otherwise they remain a mere reduction of entropy without any trace of linguistic information, teleonomy, concepts, or projects.

Information, projects, programs, and plans are the basis
of hierarchical systems. But they are independent entities,
just as energy (= matter) and time are independent
entities. Concepts can be introduced into and then transmitted by reduced entropy sequences, such as "AND,"
"OG," or " · · · · - - - - · · ". Concepts are not, however, formed by molecular movements (deviations), but
are inserted onto matter by the rectification of molecular
movements. Chance *left to itself* produces only randomness and nothing else. If one brings rectification (which
might include information and therefore logos) into the
equation, then the situation becomes totally changed, for
rectification destroys chance and may introduce information, projects, and programs. These entities may
then be stored or transmitted by imposing them onto
symbols, sequences, and order, such as make up
language. Thus symbols and sequences ("AND" and
"OG") are, so to say, empty "wagons" into which meaning, projects, information, and programs can be loaded
like coals onto a cart. Knowledge of "cart" construction
(which in our example can occur by chance and rectification of random selection) does not suffice to fill the
"cart" with coals. The "coals" (information, projects,
program, and meaning) which we load onto our "cart"
are not produced in the same "factory" as the "cart"
itself. The cart is in fact like our gramophone. The music
in the gramophone is like the coals in the cart. Thus
Eigen's genetic code, which is supposed to have been
formed by chance and rules of play, is really by analogy
only an empty "cart" or "gramophone" lacking all

genetic information ("coals" or "music").

At the moment, however, our problem is not that of the information of sequences nor even of chemical sequences ("carts"), but of the origin of language, information, meaning, teleonomy, plan, projects, and programs. Why do certain sequences of the four chemical letters of the genetic code bear meaning and projects? Whence came this meaning? Why do certain cells develop into plants, others into amoebae, frogs, crocodiles, or even human beings? Why can the code be translated and put into effect, just as a language can be realized in its translation because it bears meaning in itself? The genetic system itself is a "cart" of the most complicated sort (i.e., of highly reduced entropy). The spontaneous chance synthesis of such a system is, therefore, highly improbable. *The vital point is that chance is not at all capable of producing the projects, the linguistic information, and conventions carried by the genetic framework.*

Eigen covertly admits just this fact by pointing out that his sequences formed by chance do not contain *information in the full sense of the word* and according to the principles of modern information theory. But he admits this fact in a manner which will hardly be recognized by the average reader. His unobtrusive statement on this point in reality conceals his basic materialistic thesis. He well knows that his chance sequences and rules of play produce no genuine information (that is, projects, programs, and teleonomy). But in order to conceal this very serious theoretical and practical gap in materialistic views, he claims that real *meaning and information within the sequences only appear in the translation of the same!* We must therefore ask some further urgent questions: How was the translation apparatus formed which will extract the information from an informationless sequence such as "AND" formed by chance? The reply is immediate: also by chance alone! Thus we have now a superb translation apparatus within the biological cell which can translate meaningless sequences into meaning and which was synthesized by meaningless chance! First it was formed by chance and then it was found to be capable of "translating" meaningless, chance sequences bearing no content so as to provide them with meaning, projects, teleonomy, programs, and conventions during the process of "translation." All this by chance!

Eigen's randomly developed "translation apparatus" which produces new, creative, project-carrying information, is of course, a *contradiction in terms,* for it must be firstly a real super machine, yet was formed by chance, and secondly is allegedly capable of creating *new* information, instead of merely transferring existing information from one code into another. Of course, this machine does not really translate. It is a creation machine for information production—all produced by chance! It is just too good to be true! The only suitable scientific comment on a postulate of this sort is: Preposterous! It can simply be said that the only connection with information theory that Eigen's postulate displays is its contradiction of most of the known facts of information theory.[4]

Translation

Translation of information from one language into another constitutes one of the most difficult tasks which can be presented to a computer. The computer must be fed very carefully with extensive and highly complicated programs, if it is to carry out the translation satisfactorily. Americans have spent millions of dollars in the attempt to obtain machine translations from Russian into English automatically from computers. After more than twenty years of work, there still exists no machine which is capable of independently translating idiomatic Russian into idiomatic English without being constantly checked by a good interpreter who continually supervises the machine's work.

---

[4]Noam Chomsky (personal communication) believes that the origin of concept and information is a last "mystery," something with which the human mind cannot come to terms.

The mechanized translation of idioms from one language to another is so difficult that preprogramming of the machine seldom suffices.

In order to illustrate some of these difficulties, consider the English expression "until the cows come home" for translation into a foreign language. If a machine receives this sentence for translation from English into Russian, and the translator takes the mention of the word "cows" literally, the translation will certainly be wrong, for here the word "cows" is, of course, employed idiomatically, i.e., it is not used in the literal, but in the figurative sense of the word. Translation is thus a very difficult task, especially when idioms are involved. A machine thinks with mathematical precision. A language can, too, be mathematically precise. But it is often at the same time idiomatic and expresses itself figuratively (not mathematically). Thus painstaking idiomatic preprogramming is required if machine translation is to be reasonably successful.

Is it therefore permissible for any scientist (not to mention a leading one) to state that a translation machine, which in all scientific experience requires careful preprogramming in order to translate at all, can be formed by nonprogram, that is, by chance? Propositions of this sort can be nothing but misleading, as well as unscientific. But the situation degenerates still further when Eigen postulates that his *translation machine* was formed by chance without any program or teleonomy—and that it not only *translates* information, but in addition *produces* information during the alleged "translation" of intrinsically meaningless sequences. Thus such a machine must act not only as a computer-translator, but also as a creator and interpreter—all this without the involvement of any concept . . . by chance! For the "chance" genetical sequences which must be "translated" originally contained intrinsically neither real meaning nor genuine information. Thus, the postulated translation mechanism must not only *translate* noninformation, it must *produce* simultaneously both information and concepts. Thus the translation machine produced by Eigen's chance and rules of play must be more efficient and of greater reduced entropy than all other computers ever built by the concepts developed by man. Furthermore, it was allegedly programmed by chance—which is the antithesis of programming! We are of the opinion that the materialists' emergency brake—chance—is more than overloaded by theories of this type.

Summary

1. The reduced entropy sequences obtained by Eigen's bead games possess no information or content and lack any linguistic teleonomy.

2. Such sequences cannot be translated at all—even though Eigen alleges this—for they contain neither information, programs, projects, instructions, nor teleonomy capable of being translated.

3. The postulate of a translation mechanism which translates lack of meaning and noncontent (that is, nonsense) into information (that is, meaning) such as suggested by Eigen, cannot be taken seriously from a scientific point of view, for it would have to develop new information or projects from nonsense which would not constitute translation in the accepted sense of the word. Such a mechanism would have to be in fact a "logos" produced by chance—which merely constitutes further materialistic nonsense or intellectual suicide.

4. For this reason, the concept of the formation of a primeval programmed cell aided by a spontaneously developed machine is a plain anachronism made necessary to bolster up scientific materialistic philosophical nonsense.

Chapter 6

Time Spans and Dating Methods
Their Relation to the Question of Intelligence And the Origin of Species
Time Spans and Dating

The roles played by intelligence, information, and teleonomy in the problem of biogenesis are today the subject of intensive research. Leading biologists still attribute the generation of information machines and concepts during the development of the genetic code to chance and to the ateleonomic laws of nature. Accepting this proposition has far reaching consequences in the area of intelligence and concepts and their role in biogenesis and evolution. Let us examine a few of them.

Intelligence

If a project is guided and carried through with the aid of intelligence, less time is usually required to execute the project than if it is only "guided" or controlled by chance (the antipode of intelligence). This is, of course, a well known basic fact. Weak intelligence (or chance) nearly always requires more time to carry out any teleonomic project than high intelligence. Construction of a machine or designing a blue print with the aid of low intelligence needs more time than that needed by high intelligence to execute the same project. Expressed differently, "hit or miss" is usually more time consuming than a highly intelligent attempt to synthesize a plan, a machine, or a program. Chance itself, that is pure randomness, needs more time for constructing any project, or plan, as we have already seen, unless supported by the information (intelligence, decision-making) provided by a machine.

For example, a fairly intelligent engineer could build a small car from scratch by himself in his own workshop within, let us say, three years. Higher intelligence, plus more energy could do the job in less time. If, however, infinite intelligence (i.e., decision-making) and energy were somehow available for the construction of the same car, it could—from a theoretical point of view at least—be completed instantaneously. Infinite intelligence and energy, if such could seriously be reckoned with, would require infinitely little time to execute their projects.

A step in the opposite direction will reveal a similar mathematical situation. If the construction of the same car were left to pure chance, i.e. effectively to nonintelligence, to the antipode of intelligence, an infinite length of time would be required to bring the car project to completion. And if the car's construction were left to almost infinitely weak intelligence (i.e., practically to chance) as we have seen, an almost infinite amount of time would be required to build it. The relationship between time and intelligence in completing teleonomic projects is inversely proportional. Construction of a house with a vibrator would take longer than building a house with intelligence, although the energy of the vibrator might possibly come in useful during the process—provided its energy were rectified.

To influence the intelligence-time relationship, the separate car components could be so built that they irreversibly slot into one another when they are shaken by a vibrator. That is, when chance acts upon the car components, just as the parts of a jigsaw puzzle might irreversibly slot into each other when they are put into a vibrator, thus putting the puzzle together to form a picture with the aid of chance shaking, thus with the car. With the aid of such "irreversible" car or puzzle components chance vibration could, from a superficial point of view, build a car or solve a puzzle within a useful period of time. This sort of car component would under the circumstances behave like the pieces of the irreversible jigsaw puzzle which formed a picture of the Matterhorn when shaken.

Would a jigsaw of this type prove that chance alone is capable of carrying out a project without the aid of intelligence? No, for within the bounds of our illustration, chance has not in itself executed the project, but rather preprogramming, decision-making, irreversibility, and prior intelligence concealed within the individually interlocking pieces have done so. Programming, decision-making and intelligence acted beforehand by prefabricating the interlocking irreversible puzzle pieces or car components. Precisely such irreversible components are never built with the aid of chance, but with decision-making and planning. Thus if a puzzle or a car of this sort is built from these irreversibly interlocking pieces, it can never be said that they were built by chance. Chance certainly provided the unrectified energy required for the task, but intelligence and decision-making stored in the component parts rectified this energy at the interlocking of the programmed pieces. Thus intelligence, rectification, decision-making, thought, and teleonomy were concealed within the components; chance revealed these hidden properties in its apparent ability to produce projects. Chance did not plan or prepare the construction; it was only the executor of a preconceived, stored plan and was of secondary importance; previously invested stored decisions, intelligence played the primary role.

If the building blocks of biological life, the amino acids, phosphates, and nucleotides were built so that they automatically slotted themselves into projects, machines, and the genetic code by means of random "shaking" (i.e., by simple molecular movement), this would signify that they were built in the same way as our irreversibly interlocking car components or puzzle pieces. Chance does not build any projects at all on its own. It may "build" such if the components on which it works are "slotted." For this reason, intelligence and teleonomy must previously have carried out stored decision work on the components of the biological genetic code, enabling them to build the project of the genetic "machine," if mere chemical "shaking" is to be effective in constructing the genetic code. If a project is to be built by chance, project and intelligence must previously have acted somewhere on the components of this project. However, the plain scientific fact remains, that the amino acids and other chemical components of life do not irreversibly interlock to build living products when they are "shaken." Experiment shows that chance does not produce genes, therefore the gene components do not contain stored decisions to build genes whenever chance acts on them.

Prevailing scientific-biological philosophy of today postulates very long time spans so that chance (nonteleonomy, nonintelligence) can execute the projects of archbiopoesis. No matter how long the time spans are that one allows, chance will produce nothing in the way of machines or projects unless intelligence or teleonomy has worked on the components. However, in reality Neodarwinian theory does not require merely long time spans to produce projects from chance. It postulates *infinitely* long time spans to complete almost infinitely large projects by means of infinitely weak intelligence (chance). It is precisely this infinite amount of time which is hardly available for biological projects. For perfect chance will certainly require infinite time and infinite amounts of matter to complete any teleonomic project—neither of which are available.

In order to accomplish almost infinitely complex biological projects with the aid of infinitely weak intelligence (chance), additional infinite amounts of the basic biological components of life (i.e., of *optically active* amino acids, of nucleotides, etc.) would have to be freely available. However, these infinitely great amounts of the basic components of life (such as optically pure amino acids) do not exist within our inorganic universe—let alone on our prebiotic earth. Facts of this sort destroy entirely the credibility of the basic concepts of biogenesis according to Neodarwinian materialistic philosophy.

Thus chance does not only require an infinite amount of time to complete highly complex projects, it also needs an (almost) infinite supply of matter (optically active amino acids, etc.) which is not available for chance to work upon. For these reasons chance has no prospect at all of completing the highly complex projects of the life machine over a restricted period of time with insufficient suitable matter. Intelligence operates far more economically with time and raw materials. Infinite billions of years and an infinite universe filled with unlimited masses of suitable biological raw materials would be the required prerequisites for constructing the machine of life, the project of a genetic code and the concept of an extremely complex machine solely with the aid of chance (i.e., nonintelligence).

Let us now examine to what extent the infinite time spans that would be required for the development of a biological project by chance are actually available. We need not consider the existence of infinite masses of matter; for obviously such masses of pure optically active amino acids and other building blocks of life did not exist on the prebiotic earth.

Let us assume for a moment that a primeval cell has been formed by chemical evolution and chance according to Neodarwinian theory and that it carries out normal reproductive processes. According to evolutionary theory natural selection and mutations will slowly lead to the development of new higher species. For this to occur, basically random behavior and further large time spans are mandatory. The evolution of the dinosaur will, according to Neodarwinian views, provide us with data on the large time spans absolutely necessary for transformism (evolution of one species into another).

Dinosaurs, Trilobites, and Man

It is generally taught that dinosaurs became extinct 70-120 million years ago, that is, long before the appearance of human beings. According to Louis Leakey's most recent estimates, the immediate predecessors of man developed approximately 1-10 million years ago.[1] During the approximate 70-120 million years after the dinosaurs became extinct, chance and selection worked on the development of new mammals and of man from existing biological stock. The predecessors of Homo sapiens were supposedly among these new species so produced. Evolution from the primeval cell up to present-day man by selection and by chance required allegedly approximately 600-700 million or more years. Are these figures supported by experimental geology?

In Glen Rose near the Paluxy River (Texas) innumerable footprints of various dinosaurs can still be seen in the chalk today. The huge footprints of Brontosaurus, weighing about 70 tons, are still clearly preserved in many places. There, too, Tyrannosaurus Rex tracks can be found. The Brontosaurus footprints are perhaps the most impressive among all the other dinosaur prints. When filled with water, a small child could easily take a bath in them.

Several geologists and other scientists have found what appear to be human footprints quite near to these dinosaur footprints in the chalk, which they photographed and duly published.[2] A film exists on some of these discoveries[3] and attracted much attention in the USA.

How are we to interpret such discoveries? If they are factual it would appear that Brontosaurus existed contemporaneously with man, which is, of course, absolute heresy from a Neodarwinian view. After the formation of

---

[1] L. Leakey, *New Scientist,* Feb. 27, 1975, p. 503. *cf* L. Leakey, *Science* 192, May 14, 1976, p. 685.

[2] R. T. Bird: *Natural History* (1939) p. 96, 225, 261, 302. *cf* also A. E. Wilder Smith: *Man's Origin, Man's Destiny,* Hänssler Verlag, Neuhausen, D-7303, Stuttgart, W. Germany.

[3] S. Taylor: *Footprints in Stone.* Films for Christ Assn. (North Eden Rd., Elmwood, IL, 1974).

the dinosaur footprints in the then soft chalk, the chalk could not once again after millions of years have become soft so as to be able to receive later human footprints without at the same time damaging or eradicating the earlier dinosaur footprints. The human footprints and the dinosaur tracks are both equally clearly imprinted on the chalk, so that interim softening is out of the question. We can draw only one conclusion: the Brontosaurus and the human footsteps were formed simultaneously. If this is true, then humans and dinosaurs must have been contemporaries. If, however, according to present-day popular geological assumptions, the dinosaurs really did become extinct 70-120 million years ago, then man must already have existed 70-120 million years ago. The only alternative is that the dinosaurs still lived 1-10 million years ago—which the average geologist will scarcely admit —or that the allegedly human tracks are faked. The consequences of these alternatives are far reaching.

If, according to Darwinian theory, man developed via the amphibians, the reptiles, and the mammals, then this development must have required a great deal of time. However if man lived at the same time as the dinosaurs, he must himself either be as young or as old as they are. If he is as old as they are alleged to be, his evolutionary family tree will have automatically been reduced by some 70-120 million years. Precisely this time span reduction of the evolutionary tree cannot, however, be reconciled with Darwin's theory of evolution. His entire ladder from primeval cell to man required at the very least 600-700 million years in order to allow development of the primeval cell up to man by chance and selection. If man, however, lived at the same time as the dinosaurs, then approximately 20% of the required evolutionary time span has been lost. But just this reduction by 20% is fatal according to mathematical probability theories on an evolution based on chance and selected mutations. If man and the dinosaur are considered to be geologically equally young, other grave problems arise for the evolutionary tree.

Several scientists have attempted to circumvent the problem posed by contemporaneous human and dinosaur footprints, by claiming that the human footprints near Glen Rose were faked, that is that they were chiseled into the chalk to deceive geologists and others. However, recent discoveries of other new human footprints series in a virgin (i.e., freshly excavated) layer of chalk eliminate this solution.

Other scientists, e.g., George Gaylord Simpson in the USA, claim that the entire discovery at Glen Rose does not exist, that it is simply a lie—a fake—just as was the Piltdown man, who was, of course, deliberately planted by reputable geologists possibly in the interests of humor or of Darwinism! Fraud and deceit occur even among scientists, just as they do among other fallible mortals, so that this explanation of the discoveries at Glen Rose is certainly technically feasible. But there is one snag to it. Discoveries in a similar vein have been made elsewhere, even if they are usually not mentioned in the official publishing media. Naturally great caution must be exercised before accepting any discoveries such as the Piltdown man or the Glen Rose finds for scientists are as fallible as any other mortals are. One fact remains certain in questions of this type: the entire Neodarwinian philosophy would be totally *destroyed by one proven discovery of a single brontosaurus track contemporaneous with a single human track in the same virgin layer of chalk.* Such considerations could well explain the militant attitude of Neodarwinians toward the Glen Rose finds. G. G. Simpson labels them as a plain lie. The authenticity of the discoveries at Glen Rose would in one blow absolutely and radically destroy Simpson's lifetime's work as a proponent of Neodarwinism. The well known publishing scandals involving Macmillan and the suppression of Velikowski's research, as well as the Piltdown hoax, provide us with much food for thought in respect to the suppression of the publication of facts which would correct erroneous generally accepted scientific philosophies.

Reduction of the time available for the evolution of the Darwinian human family tree has, however, become even more drastic within the last twenty years or so. According to present day estimates the trilobites became extinct approximately 300 million years ago. This opinion leads to the conclusion that all geological formations containing trilobites must be at least 300 million years old. However, any formations containing human footprints should be approximately only 1-10 million years old, according to modern Neodarwinian teachings, so that formations containing trilobites can under no circumstances contain traces of human activity.

Dr. Clifford Burdick, geologist, reported on a remarkable discovery some time ago, which calls the above into question.[4] In Swasey Mountain, west central Utah, at an altitude of approximately 2,000 feet the footprints of a barefooted child were discovered in a Wheeler formation. In the middle of the track's arch lay the compressed remains of a trilobite. Obviously the trilobite was not fossilized when the child stepped on it, for the organism was squashed by the child. Thus Clifford Burdick assumes that the trilobite was not yet fossilized at the time the track arose. If the assumptions made by Dr. Burdick are correct, human beings and trilobites must have lived contemporaneously, which is, of course, for any true blooded Neodarwinian, simply idiotic.

If the trilobites became extinct approximately 300 million years ago, then man's evolutionary tree of life time span is further reduced by approximately 400 million years. In this case man must have developed from the primitive primeval cell at an enormous rate, in fact in a few years, for he was apparently more or less fully developed at the time of the trilobites! Of course, chance and natural selection are not capable of having worked at this speed without the aid of intelligence. No scientist could believe that man developed over a relatively small number of years on the basis of natural selection and chance mutations.

---

[4] cf A. E. Wilder Smith. *Basis for a New Biology*. Telos Verlag (Neuhausen-Stuttgart, 1975) p. 217 ff.-Personal communication. cf. *Science News,* Feb. 2, 1974, Vol. 105, p. 72.

Some time ago, caves were discovered[5] containing drawings depicting human beings in the presence of certain animals. Some of these animals have a curious dinosaur-like appearance! Might this fact again point in the same direction? Might early man not have lived together with all sorts of animal species—including dinosaurs? If, that is, the Neodarwinian interpretation of geology happens to be fallacious? Some of the animals depicted in these cave drawings show a remarkable resemblance to the dragons described with such gusto in ancient fables and myths for children. A final conclusion cannot and may not be drawn here, for the evidence concerning these drawings is still incomplete. However, should such discoveries be confirmed, then the enormous time spans required for the human evolutionary ancestral tree after the principles of chance and selection are lacking. If these enormous time spans are myths, then biological evolution according to Darwinian principles is simply a myth, too.

If the dating methods used to set up the family tree of life are uncertain or erroneous, this might throw light on the remarkable paleontological discoveries described above. For this reason we must now examine more closely the customary paleontological dating methods, for on them depends the entire experimental and philosophical structure of modern biology. If these methods are unreliable or even fallacious, then the entire Neodarwinian biological philosophy of evolution automatically also becomes unreliable or fallacious with them.

Dating Methods

During the last 10 or 15 years new fossilized hominoid (manlike) remains have been discovered throughout the world, especially in East Africa. The Leakey family has been a pioneering factor in this work. These discoveries

---

[5] cf E. T. Scoyen: *Arizona Highways* (July, 1951) 36-39.

are considered to present evidence for the development of man from his alleged animal ancestors though they have overthrown most of the older evolutionary schemes on man's alleged animal ancestry. We are thinking especially of Leakey's work in the Olduvai Gorge, which has been reported on in various scientific media.[6] Naturally the age attributed to these new fossil discoveries depends entirely on the methods of dating employed. If Leakey's datings are uncertain, then his conclusions are equally uncertain.

According to Leakey's more recent reports, the hominids (manlike primates) appeared much earlier in geological time than commonly assumed 10-30 years ago. In those days it was assumed that man (Homo sapiens) differentiated himself from other hominids approximately one million years ago. Thus, from a geological point of view, Homo sapiens was very young. Since the work of Leakey, 1-10 million years in geological time are considered to be a more accurate estimate for this evolutionary branching. The dating methods used to determine the age are, of course, absolutely vital to all theories involved. Yet very little is said in the scientific publications we cite about the actual dating methods employed. Herein lies the weak point in all Leakey's otherwise excellent discoveries.

Establishment geology regarded Leakey's discoveries with extreme skepticism at first. For they entirely destroyed the older evolutionary human family trees which had been set up with so much hard work and publicity. Of even greater importance, of course, was the hard fact that Leakey's discoveries removed up to 10 million years of available evolutionary time for the evolution of man, for Leakey proposes that man and his immediate predecessors developed several million years *earlier* than

[6]L. Leakey: Skull 1470. *National Geographic Magazine* 143 (1973) 819. Start Again on Man's Family Tree. *Science News* 105 (1974) 69; *New Scientist* (Feb. 27, 1975) 503; *Science* 192 (May 14, 1976).

previously assumed. This early appearance of man requires, of course, a more rapid evolution by chance than most serious scientists would hold to be credible. Chance demands a decidedly slow evolution rate. Leakey's discoveries, however, require an almost unbelievably rapid human development from other primates by mutation and selection. For this reason, the reservations of conservative scientists regarding Leakey's work are understandable. We must, therefore, ask ourselves how Leakey and others carried out their datings, for everything depends on the reliability of these measurements.

Index Fossils

How are geological formations generally dated? One important method for determining the age of formations containing fossils is known as the Index Fossil Method. The types of fossil remains discovered in a geological layer are first examined. Then, according to the fossil content of the formation, the age of the same is determined, i.e., the index fossils present determine the formation's age. If, for example, dinosaur bones, eggs, or footprints appear in a geological formation, the geologist assumes that the formation involved originated during the lifetime of dinosaurs, at least 70-120 million years ago. Thus, the fossil content of a formation is decisive in determining the age of a formation by the index fossil method. Consequently, according to this method of dating, all formations containing brontosaurus or other dinosaur footprints must be at least 70-120 million years old.

If a formation contains fossilized trilobite remains this formation must, by the same considerations, be approximately 300 million years old, for trilobites became extinct approximately 300 million years ago (according to Neodarwinian theory). Discovery in any geological formation of human remains (bones, footprints, tools) informs us that the formation must be geologically modern. Man developed only 1-10 million years ago (according to Leakey). Human remains and formations containing the same cannot, of course, be older than man himself.

This index fossil method of dating is considered by most modern geologists to be absolutely authoritative and decisive, even though a little reflection shows that a prerequisite for its reliability is the reliability of the entire Neodarwinian theory of evolution. If the concepts of evolutionary theory are uncertain, then all datings obtained by the index fossil method are equally uncertain. Darwinians claim that the trilobites became extinct approximately 300 million years ago. Thus all formations containing trilobites must accordingly be approximately 300 million years old.

In reality, the index fossil method serves as a classic example of circular thought, for it accepts the assumptions of evolutionary theory (that in the past man slowly, over huge time spans, evolved from the primitive ancestors of dinosaurs and other species) in order to determine the age of man and of other organisms. It accepts transformism (the development of one species into another) as a fact in order to prove and to determine that this transformism occurred in geological time.

Naturally, the same principles of the index fossil method are applied when dating other geological formations. Thus, because trilobites are said to be geologically relatively primitive organisms (their eye was in actual fact the most sophisticated eye ever seen in all history[7]), according to evolutionary concept, they must be geologically old. Such arguments overlook the fact that physiologically primitive organisms such as amoeba still exist today as contemporaries of highly developed organisms, such as man or apes. Geological age and physiological primitiveness are by no means coupled. If only physiologically primitive organisms, such as trilobites, appear within a geological formation, this does not signify that only primitive organisms (like trilobites) existed when they were deposited in the formation involved, for the formations involved were usually deposited by water. Sessile animals

---

[7]*Science News,* Feb. 2, 1974, 105, p. 72.

and plants (with a fixed location) are reached by the water and fossilized on the spot, whereas more complex organisms (such as those with legs or wings) can escape the oncoming water. Thus a formation deposited by water contains mainly those organisms which could not escape from the water at their time of death. The first organisms reached by the water were, therefore, often the physiologically most primitive types—and not necessarily those that were geologically older or more primitive.

The use of the index fossil dating method also involves other dangers which put the reliability of its results in question. When I was studying zoology at the University of Oxford (1933), Coelacanthus (Latimeria), a type of fish, was known as a fossil. According to the theories of those days, it acted as a sort of missing link in the evolution of fish. Geological formations containing fossilized remains of Latimeria were dated with apparent certainty using Coelacanthus as an index fossil. Depending on the opinion of the scientist involved concerning the time at which Latimeria became extinct, the formation containing Latimeria was dated.

Today most biologically informed persons know that any datings carried out using Latimeria as an index fossil may be completely erroneous, for exactly the same fish has recently been repeatedly caught—very much alive—off the shores of Madagascar.[8] The live fish is identical with the fossil ones which are supposedly some millions of years old. If Latimeria really had become extinct approximately 70 million years ago, then its fossilized remains could have been used as a means of dating. But today who could claim that a formation containing Latimeria really must be 70 million years old? The remains could equally well have stemmed from some of those Latimeria individuals which were swimming around Madagascar in

---

[8]Coelacanthus, *Science News,* March 27, 1965, p. 199; *New Scientist,* May 25, 1972, p. 427; *New Scientist,* May 27, 1976, Vol. 70, p. 456.

geologically modern times.

Thus the reliability of the index fossil method depends entirely on the time at which the species involved became extinct. If, however, this date cannot be determined with certainty, which is the case, as Kerkut so rightly points out,[9] then this method cannot provide us with any precise dates at all. The index fossil method cannot provide us with any absolute values as long as absolute dates of extinction are unknown. All the results which the method supplies depend on the validity of the family trees themselves, that is in the final analysis on the concepts of evolutionary theory. Again dating the family tree is carried out with the aid of merely assumed times of extinction.

While considering the problem of Latimeria we must not overlook a further aspect of the misleading nature of evolutionary theory. Latimeria was considered to be a fairly primitive fish, an ancestor of more highly developed later species. Only lately a quite different attitude toward Latimeria has arisen, for it has been found that in its organization, Latimeria is not such a primitive species after all, for the fish is ovoviviparous, i.e., it bears living offspring—although without the aid of a placenta as found in mammals.[10] How must we regard the fact that a fish which was considered relatively primitive and underdeveloped on the evolutionary scale displays such a highly developed reproductory mechanism? Certain modern sharks reproduce in a similar manner. How can certain fish which are supposed to have appeared so early *geologically,* be so highly developed *physiologically?* The same problem arises concerning the trilobite's sophisticated eye, as we have already seen. Evolution aided by

---

[9]G. A. Kerkut, *Implications of Evolution,* Pergamon Press (London) 2nd edition, 1977, Chapter 9 on "Vertebrate Paleontology," p. 134-49.

[10]*New Scientist,* 70 (1976) 456.

chance and selection hardly would have had time to accomplish physiological finesses of this sort. The highly developed eye of the trilobites underlines the same fact very firmly.[11]

In Glen Rose (Texas) immense numbers of dinosaur footprints are to be found in the bed of the Paluxy River[12] as we have already mentioned. Because the dinosaur footprints serve as index fossils, the chalk formation at Glen Rose is ascribed an age of 70-120 million years. However, Roland Bird and other Neodarwinian scientists photographed Brontosaurus and what appear to be human footprints at Glen Rose. The apparently human footprints were often 16 and more inches (39 cm) long, although some adjacent prints had a length of about 12 inches (30 cm). Further tracks exist or existed at Glen Rose which correspond to a human child's foot in size. If these footprints are really human—and there exist no *experimental* reasons to question this assumption, for R. T. Bird dug out specimens of various types and took them with him after carefully photographing them—then we have struck upon yet another considerable difficulty with dating methods, for the man-like footprints lie in the same formation as the dinosaur prints. Fig. 4 reproduces a photograph of some of these tracks.

In view of these facts, how are we to approach the problem of dating the Glen Rose formations? According to the index fossil method these formations containing dinosaur prints must therefore be between 70 and 120 million years old. But judging by the human footprints, the same formation has a maximum age of 1-10 million years (according to Leakey's dating) for it contains human traces.

---

[11]*New Scientist,* 69 (1975) 600; *Science News,* Feb. 2, 1974, 105, p. 72.

[12]A. E. Wilder Smith: *Man's Origin, Man's Destiny,* Hänssler Verlag, D-7303, Neuhausen-Stuttgart, F.G.R.

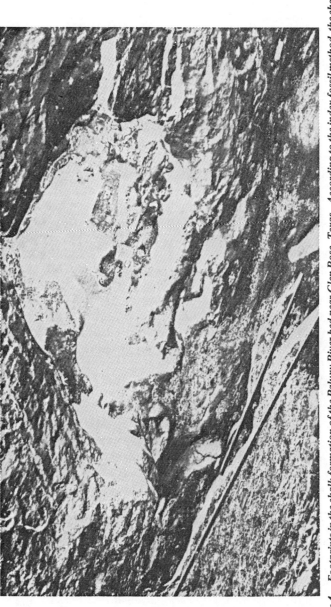

Figure 4. Footprints in the chalk formation of the Paluxy River bed near Glen Rose, Texas. According to the index fossil method, the chalk formation is given an age of 70-120 million years due to the great numbers of dinosaur footprints. At Glen Rose Brontosaurus footprints (above center) appear together with prints which can be interpreted as human footprints (top left, near center of picture edge: adult print; bottom right: possible child's footprint; note measuring rods and size differences). Dated according to the "human" footprints, the formation has an age of 1-10 million years. If these finds are genuine, they would prove that dinosaurs and man lived as contemporaries or that the index fossil method is not suitable for dating geological formations. (Photo: Stanley E. Taylor)

Which dating figure is correct?

The experimental side of Darwinian evolutionary theory is heavily dependent on the dating of the fossilized biological remains. For evolutionary theory to be experimentally acceptable, one or more dating methods independent of evolutionary theory and its teachings would have to be available.

Certainly the index fossil method is the most important method for the dating of formations known to modern geology. It has served more than all other dating methods to establish evolutionary theory. It must be remembered that, as applied today, it *always* supports evolutionary theory! Of course, the reason for this is by now perfectly clear: the method assumes that evolutionary theory is experimentally correct so that a suitable family tree can be set up depending on evolutionary concepts. Then it confirms the veracity of the evolutionary theory on the basis of the evolutionary family tree . . . that is, the index fossil method is calibrated against the theory of evolution . . . then it proceeds to calibrate evolutionary theory against the index fossil method. Is it surprising that the theory of evolution confirms the index fossil method and vice versa? Neodarwinian theory has been thriving on this circular thinking between theory and practice and practice and theory for over 130 years. The index fossil method has significantly served to keep evolutionary theory in its scientific saddle,[13] despite the fact that Neodarwinism itself is, in addition to the above contradictions, also a direct contradiction of the second law of thermodynamics.

Discarding the index fossil method would eliminate a major stay of evolutionary theory, which has by now held up more than 130 years of biological research. It should be considered as discredited today.

---

[13]R. H. Rastall, "Geology," *Encyclopaedia Britannica* (1956), X. 168. *cf Man's Origin, Man's Destiny,* Telos, Hänssler Verlag, p. 128; CLP Publishers, San Diego, CA 92115.

The C^{14} Dating Method

The C^{14} dating method can be applied whenever carbon-containing biological remains are involved. Carbon consists of a mixture of isotopes (elements with different atomic weights but identical chemical properties): C^{11}, C^{12}, C^{13}, and C^{14}. C^{14} is synthesized by the bombardment of nitrogen (N^{14}) by slow or thermal neutrons in the upper atmosphere:

$$N^{14} + n = C^{14} + H^1$$

As cosmic rays constantly bombard the earth's atmosphere which contains much N^{14}, C^{14} is continually formed in the upper atmosphere from N^{14}. Unlike C^{12}, this C^{14} is radioactive. When this radioactive C^{14} combines with oxygen, $C^{14}O_2$ is formed, which is of course, also radioactive. The radioactive carbon dioxide $C^{14}O_2$ mixes with the nonradioactive carbon dioxide ($C^{12}O_2$) in the air.

C^{14} decays radioactively. In 5568 years (or 5730 years according to some scientists) half the amount of C^{14} present in any sample will have decayed. Thus the half-life of C^{14} is said to be 5568 (5730) years. After this time the radioactivity of any amount of C^{14} in any sample will have decreased to one half of the original value. After a further 5568 (5730) years the amount of radioactivity will have halved again. After a third half-life, the value will again have halved, etc.

When a plant absorbs carbon dioxide from the air and reduces it to sugar and starch during photosynthesis with the aid of sunlight, the entire plant tissue will become just as radioactive as the carbon dioxide in the air: for the plant and the air both contain C^{14} in a state of equilibrium. Animals and human beings eat the radioactive C^{14} containing plants, so that their tissues also become radioactive. All forms of life are finally dependent on the (radioactive) CO_2 in the air, and all life is in equilibrium with this radioactive CO_2 in the air. Thus as long as C^{14} is synthesized at a constant rate from N^{14} in the air by cosmic bombardment, the level of radioactivity in the air and within the entire living spectrum of biology will remain constant. Biology and the air are in a dynamic state of equilibrium.

The death of an animal or a plant will terminate the equilibrium between the C^{14} in the air and the C^{14} in the organism's tissue, for in a dead organism the C^{14} within the tissue is no longer renewed by C^{14} in the air. The radio-active C^{14} molecules in the dead tissue now decay without being replaced by new C^{14} from the air. Consequently, the C^{14} radioactivity of a dead organism decreases (whereas it remains constant within a living organism, i.e. in equilibrium with the C^{14} concentration in the air). 5568 (5730) years after the organism's death the radioactivity in the dead tissues is therefore exactly one half of the original value. This process constitutes the basis of the C^{14} method of dating. The C^{14} radioactivity of the dead tissue is determined and, using the known half life, the number of years that have elapsed since the organism's death can be calculated. This procedure is, of course, based on the assumption that the air's C^{14} radioactivity has remained constant from the organism's time of death up to the present day. The reliability of the C^{14} dating method depends, then, on the following factors.

C^{14} In The Air

The concentration of C^{14} in the air must have been identical at the organism's time of death and at the time of dating. If, for example, the C^{14} level in the air was zero when the organism died, and 1,000 years have passed since its death, then the remains of this organism will appear to be infinitely old today, for at its death it contained no C^{14} whatsoever; therefore, at any and all times it will register an infinite age by this method.

However, if the C^{14} radioactivity of an organism which died 5568 (5730) years ago was exactly twice its present value, modern C^{14} dating 5568 years later would show that this organism died zero years ago, even though it died 5568 years ago, for just half of its activity at death has disappeared. We must conclude that the reliability of the C^{14} method of dating depends on a constant rate of C^{14} synthesis by cosmic radiation in the upper atmosphere, from the time of the death of the organism until the dating.

Rate of C^{14} Decay

The rate of C^{14} decay must remain constant under all environmental conditions, i.e. absolute half life constancy must be certain under all environmental conditions. In certain specialist circles doubts have arisen on this point.[14]

Exchange of C^{12} and C^{14} Within the Fossils

After the organism's death absolutely no further exchange of C^{14} and C^{12} between the environment and the organic remains may take place. If for example fresh C^{14} in the form of carbonate or bicarbonate diffuses into the sample which is to be dated, obviously the remains will appear to be younger than they really are. Conversely, if C^{14} is washed out in the form of a carbonate or bicarbonate and replaced by C^{12}, then the remains will appear older than their true age. It cannot always be guaranteed that no C^{12}/C^{14} exchange of this sort has ever occurred between death and dating.

The above conditions all affect the reliability of Libby's C^{14} method. On them depends any and all reliable dating by this method. Libby himself pointed out the possibilities of such uncertainties in his method and warned against excessively high expectations as to reliability from the same.

---

[14]John Anderson: Abstract of papers. 161st National Meeting, Amer. Chem. Soc., Los Angeles (1971). *cf* also W. W. Fields: *Unformed and Unfilled,* Presbyterian and Reformed Publishing Company (Nutley, NJ, 1976), p. 212.

Constancy of the C^{14} Concentration In the Atmosphere

As we have seen, if the C14 method of dating is to provide us with useful reliable results, the C^{14} concentration in the air must have remained constant for between 5,000 and 60,000 years. This means that C^{14} synthesis by cosmic ray bombardment in the upper atmosphere must have remained constant for thousands of years. In other words, bombardment of N^{14} by cosmic rays must be equally intense now as at the time the biological remains which are to be dated died. Can we guarantee this constancy of cosmic ray bombardment in the upper atmosphere?

Although we are by no means sure, the experts are of the opinion that the source of these cosmic rays has probably remained constant over long ages. But questions concerning the concentration and intensity of the rays reaching the upper atmosphere remain unanswered. Both depend on various factors including the strength of the earth's own magnetic field. The stronger the earth's magnetic field, the weaker will be the concentration of cosmic rays actually reaching the upper atmosphere. Conversely, the weaker the earth's magnetic field, the stronger the cosmic radiation reaching the upper atmosphere. Thus during periods of a stronger magnetic field the earth will be subject to less cosmic radiation than during periods of a weak magnetic field. Thus atmospheric C^{14} concentration depends to a large extent on the strength of the earth's magnetic field. But, as we have already discovered, the C^{14} method depends on a constant synthesis of C^{14} by cosmic rays. Thus the C^{14} method of dating finally depends on a constant magnetic field surrounding the earth. Let us consider this constant magnetic field from a practical point of view.

The Influence of the Earth's Magnetic Field on C^{14} Synthesis

It is generally known that the earth's magnetic field

is subject to large variations. One hundred and forty-five years ago Gauss began to measure the earth's magnetic field and in the year 1835 he obtained a value of 85.6 × 10^{21} Ampère/m². Today, under the same conditions we obtain a value of 80.1 × 10^{21} Ampère/m². Thus the magnetic field has fallen by 5.5 × 10^{21} Ampère/m² over a period of 145 years.[15]

The earth's magnetic field is, to a large extent, independent of the magnetic ores in the earth's surface, for it originates from the electric currents in the earth's crust. Metals cannot be magnetized at a temperature higher than the Curie temperature (for iron approx. 750°). Approx. 25 km below the crust of the earth the temperature reaches the Curie value, so that at this depth iron cannot be the cause of the magnetic field. The same, of course, applies to other magnetic metals. If the Curie temperature is reached at a depth of 25 km and if the earth's radius measures 6370 km, then the Curie temperature for all substances is certainly surpassed in the earth's interior. Hence the earth's magnetism must be due to electromagnetism and our planet is not a permanent, but an electromagnet. Electric currents within the crust develop the magnetic field, and as soon as these are eliminated or die out the magnetic field vanishes.

As, in fact, the earth's magnetic field is rapidly decreasing according to experimental data, the current within the earth's crust is obviously declining. The cause and origin of these currents have been the object of much speculation.

---

[15]W. F. Libby: *Radiocarbon Dating*. University of Chicago Press, 6th revised edition (Chicago, 1965), p. 4-5; *cf* W. W. Fields: *Unformed and Unfilled*. Presbyterian and Reformed Publ. Co. (Nutley, NJ, 1976). A. E. Wilder Smith: *Man's Origin, Man's Destiny*, Shaw Publishers (Wheaton, Ill. 1970), p. 116-118; CLP Publishers, San Diego, CA 92115.

Lamb[16] is of the opinion that we are dealing with free currents, the remains of past geological and cosmic events. Currents of this sort would, of course, decrease with time, so that the magnetic field must diminish, as far as we can see. In addition we know that in the geological past the magnetic field has fluctuated. However we know of no evidence permitting us to assume that the decline of this field by normal known processes during historical times could be transformed into an increase of the same. Restoration of the current within the earth's crust by means of geological or cosmic events during the last 20,000 years would thus seem to be out of the question. The half life of the earth's magnetic field, as determined today, lies at approximately 1400 years, if the rate of decay has remained constant. This signifies a halving of the earth's magnetic field within 1400 years. Consequently, the magnetic field will have diminished to 1/32 of its original value after 7000 years (five half life periods of 1400 years each). The present strength of the field must therefore be approximately 37% of its strength at the time of Christ.[17]

These observations have important consequences:

a. Relatively recently from a geological point of view the earth manifested a magnetic field significantly greater than that it possesses today. The stronger the earth's magnetic field, the weaker the cosmic radiation reaching the upper atmosphere and consequently the feebler the synthesis of C^{14}. Thus the progressive decline of the magnetic field serves to progressively increase C^{14} synthesis. The stronger the field, the more repressed the C^{14} synthesis.

b. The above considerations concerning the magnetic

---

[16]T. G. Barnes: *Origin and Destiny of the Earth's Magnetic Field.* Institute for Creation Research (San Diego, 1973), p. XIII: *cf* Fields (See Footnote 14).

[17]Fields (*cf* Footnote 14), p. 203.

field levels of the earth can be summarized as follows:[18]

> 4000 B.C. The field measured 12 Gauss
> 5000 B.C. 20 Gauss
> 6000 B.C. 35 Gauss
> 8000 B.C. 98 Gauss
> 1970 A.D. 0.62 Gauss

c. Hence approximately 10,000 years ago very little C^{14} may have been in the air if the decay of the magnetic field proceeded at a constant rate, for the reaction $N^{14} + n = C^{14} + H^1$ could have been practically completely inhibited due to lack of cosmic radiation.

d. Biological remains deposited 10,000 years ago will have contained little C^{14} at their death, if the above surmises are correct, so that today they automatically must appear to be far older than they really are when dated by the C^{14} method. If petroleum and coal were formed in those times under the above conditions, they will already have been radioactively "dead" when they were deposited. Thus from the C^{14} dating point of view they will appear to be extraordinarily old. Could the apparent great age of petroleum and coal according to C^{14} dating be attributed to the above propositions?

e. A further important point emerges on the following consideration: Under the protection of a strong magnetic field, not only the C^{14} radioactivity in the air would be reduced, but all ionizing radiation of cosmic origin would also be reduced on the earth's surface. Thus the earth's surface would be less radioactive than it is today under the influence of the earth's declining magnetic field.

It is a well known fact that increased amounts of ionizing radiation reduce the life span of all biological or-

---

[18]D. and Maureen Tarling: *Continental Drift.* Doubleday & Co. (Garden City, NY, 1971), p. 64: *cf* Fields (See Footnote 14), p. 64.

ganisms and impair their vitality. Simultaneously, biological mutations will increase. Thus, if a period of significantly reduced ionizing irradiation of the earth's surface ever existed, all biological organisms would at that time have tended to live longer and to undergo fewer mutations than today. They would also have possessed more vitality. The earth's carboniferous layers bear witness to an immense vitality within the plant kingdom. The gigantism among plants and animals of previous ages indicates vitality of the same sort. No doubt higher temperatures also contributed to this increased vitality. During certain periods of time in the past the climate was certainly warmer and more favorable to life than today. Yet temperature differences alone would hardly provide a sufficient explanation for the luxuriant growth of the carboniferous period with the gigantism it exhibited in plants and in animals.

We would thus expect the rapid decay of the earth's magnetic field to exert a great influence on the biological kingdom. If the rate of decline of the earth's magnetic field has remained constant, then life on the earth 10,000 years ago could have shown a significantly raised vitality, as well as having been longer living than today. Harmful mutations, due to ionizing rays would not yet have accumulated within the genes of animals and plants. For this reason unbiased biologists will read with a certain satisfaction that Adam lived for 930 years, Methuselah for 969 years, and Noah for 950 years. Only after great geological changes, which probably further impaired the magnetic field, did man's life span sink to 120 years, later to become reduced to 70 years. Conceivably the great dying and extinction of the largest species among land animals and plants commenced for similar reasons. This might certainly at least partly be attributed to decreasing protection of the earth's surface against ionizing radiation.

   f. The earth's magnetic field is generally thought to wax and to wane. The earth's magnetic poles have also been reversed from time to time. Thus the question arises whether these fluctuations of the magnetic field were connected with the extinction of various species in geological time.

Robert J. Uffen[19] suggested that the decreasing magnetic field permitted cosmic irradiation of the earth's surface to such an extent that organisms inhabiting shallow water were destroyed—or that their mutation rate became so high that evolution was thus accelerated.

Since the publication of Uffen's work, other researchers have reported that the increased cosmic irradiation resulting from a reduced magnetic field would be too weak to produce noticeable biological effects. Conversely, other researchers have shown that entire biological families became extinct during magnetic reversal.[20] The recent Deep Sea Drilling Project has discovered a connection between the dying out of various Foraminifera and field reversal.[21]

Alan V. Cox[22] developed these ideas further. If the dipole determining four-fifths or more of the magnetic flux disappears completely, protection of the earth's surface against cosmic irradiation would not decrease by more than 10% - 12%, for the main protection is not provided by the magnetic field, but by the atmosphere itself. Cox then suggests that at times of decreasing magnetic field strength, the protection provided by the atmosphere against cosmic rays also decreases. The mechanism weakening the atmospheric protection operates as follows: Lack of a magnetic field surrounding the earth would permit freer access to protons from solar activity. These protons penetrating the atmosphere during a period of decreased magnetic flux catalytically destroy the ozone layer of the upper atmosphere by producing nitrogen

---

[19]R. J. Uffen, *Nature* 198 (1963) 143. *cf Science News* 109 (1976) 204.

[20]*Geological Society of America Bulletin* 82 (1971) 2433.

[21] Barbara Keating, Emilie Passagno, and Ch. Helsley: *Science News* 109 (1976) 204.

[22]A. V. Cox: *cf Science News* 109 (1976) 204.

monoxide (NO). It is well known that NO catalytically destroys ozone. Destruction of the ozone layer would permit passage of ultra violet rays which can be fatal to living organisms. Thus a decreasing field would permit more protons from solar activity to pass, which would then form NO. NO would destroy the ozone layer protecting life from destructive ultra violet rays. In this manner the earth's magnetic field would, after all, strongly influence the life of terrestrial biological organisms.

The basis of the C^{14} dating method presupposes a constant magnetic field. But a constant decay of the above type could be assumed if the magnetism inducing current originated from one great unique geological event. Minor later events with current-producing or current-destroying effects would affect the magnitude of the current and impair the constancy of decay. As, however, we are not yet acquainted with the original source of current, one can only for the time being speculate in this area.

Some Consequences

a. Biological remains possessing a real age of 5000 - 10,000 years can simulate a far greater age when tested by C^{14} dating.

b. Increased ionizing radiation, as a consequence of a decreasing magnetic field will shorten the life span of all forms of life and reduce their vitality. Mutations will also become more frequent. As, however, over 90% of all mutations are harmful to life, the genetics of all forms of life will degenerate under these conditions. This degeneration can lead to changing forms of a species, but hardly to upward development, as degeneration cannot be equated to evolutionary upward development.

c. At times of lowered cosmic irradiation in the past, fewer mutations will have occurred than at times of increased irradiation. Now if mutations are the real source of Neodarwinian evolution (as claimed by most biologists today), then this type of evolution will occur *less quickly* during a period of stronger terrestrial magnetic flux. Under strong irradiation Neodarwinian evolution should occur more quickly.

Here we meet with a cardinal paradox of Neodarwinian thought: The conditions for Neodarwinian evolution—strong irradiation, much mutation—are precisely those which are most detrimental to life. Evolution at an early stage in the earth's history would, accordingly, have progressed far more slowly under lowered cosmic irradiation than today under strong irradiation and increased mutation. Yet geology today informs us of the contrary: The major evolutionary processes are supposed to have taken place during the Precambrian and the Cambrian, at a time when mutations due to ionizing radiation were probably scarcer than today.

Let us bear in mind additionally that at present, when all living beings are probably exposed to stronger ionizing rays than ever before, little evidence of biological upward (evolutionary) development occurs. Present-day evolution supposedly takes place on a purely mental level (in the libraries of the world?), not physically! However, the biological distinction between these two levels and types of evolution remains somewhat hazy, for from a biological point of view, mental evolution depends on the physical evolution of the wiring of the brain—or at least of the genetic code which controls the development and the programming of the brain!

d. If biological remains are, in fact, significantly younger than they appear to be according to the C^{14} and other dating methods, then the time span required for effective evolution is even shorter than we imagined. This abbreviation of time spans available for evolution is very serious in principle, for evolution with the aid of chance and mutations requires above all enormously great time spans. Here not even relatively short time spans can be forfeited or spared. The time required for effective Neodarwinian evolution by chance is theoretically far too short anyway, for such evolution requires well nigh infinite time, to say nothing of infinite masses of pure optically active starting materials.

Other Dating Methods

Due to the relatively short half-life of C^{14}, this method of dating is only employed for time spans of up to 10,000 - 60,000 years. Other dating methods have been developed for older formations and biological remains. The potassium-argon method is based on the fact that potassium is weakly radioactive and slowly breaks down to give the inert gas argon. Argon gas is then stored in the various crystal lattices containing the potassium. The amount of argon present in the potassium-containing crystal lattices is measured. Thus the age of the crystals can be calculated according to the half-life of potassium.

Applying this method, the amount of argon gas which has collected within the crystal lattice since its formation after the liquid solidified is determined. Obviously argon can only be retained within a solid crystal lattice (and not within liquid lava). Therefore, the age of liquid "rocks" (lava) cannot be determined in this manner. Only the age of a rock after its crystallization can be measured by this method.

Despite the theoretical simplicity of this dating method, its practical application leads to many difficulties. Argon is only physically trapped within the crystal lattices, so that gas can easily escape. The heating, for example, of a crystal containing argon within a formation would cause at least a part of the gas to escape. If argon escapes, the formation will of course appear younger than its actual age. Conversely the formation will appear older if argon from the air (the air contains considerable amounts of argon) penetrates into the crystal lattice. Under these circumstances (if argon has diffused into the lattices from the air), this method of dating will determine too great an age.

As micro- and nano-quantities of argon are in question, the argon method involves a high degree of experimental error. Another difficulty arises which is often not sufficiently taken into account today. It is generally assumed that the radioactive decay rate is absolutely constant. Some scientists are surprised if one questions the decay rate constant. Yet everyone knows today that the half-life of plutonium, for example, can be altered almost at will. The same applies to certain isotopes of uranium and other radioactive substances also. If the plutonium is in the environment of an atom bomb (i.e., exposed to strong neutron fluxes) the half-life of this radioactive metal may amount to a few nano-seconds instead of thousands of years. If the same metal is placed within an atomic reactor (i.e. subjected to a variable controllable neutron flux), then its half-life can be adjusted at will. If, due to cosmic events in the past, high neutron fluxes occurred on the earth's surface (e.g., before biogenesis), then it would have been possible for the half-lives of certain radioactive substances to be significantly altered. Thus today we can no longer state that the half-life of a radioactive substance is an absolute constant under all conditions. It depends on the environment. Yet all dating methods independent of the index fossil method rely on the absolute constancy of the half-lives of radioactive substances.

The surfaces of the moon and the earth clearly demonstrate how often in the past the environment on these bodies must have changed. Hence we can assume that neutron fluxes on the earth may not always have remained constant.[23]

Summary

In principle, customary methods of dating are not capable of absolutely guaranteeing the long time spans needed for evolution according to Neodarwinian thought. Rapid upward development according to evolutionary theory requires a high rate of mutation, which could depend on strong ionizing radiation. Yet we know that high doses of radiation are unfavorable to already existing

---

[23]Re: Dating Methods, *cf* also *Man's Origin, Man's Destiny, Basis for a New Biology,* and *Creation of Life.* Telos Verlag (Neuhausen—Stuttgart). *cf.* CLP Publishers, San Diego, CA 92115.

forms of life. In excessively high concentrations ionizing radiation can easily destroy life. During the Precambrian and Cambrian periods almost all biological species are represented, which would suggest a high mutatory rate according to Neodarwinian theory. This high rate of mutation would depend on intensive radioactive irradiation, which would be highly unfavorable for biogenesis. High radiation dosage prevents the formation and preservation of healthy genes; it tends to lead to involution rather than to evolution.

Finally one is forced to admit that our dating methods by means of radioactivity provide us with little really reliable data as to the enormous time spans required for evolution according to Darwin. It is relatively easy for any biological or inorganic material to simulate a great age—or no age at all!

Chapter 7

Microevolution, Transformism, And Concepts

Are Mutations and Natural Selection Sufficient to Account for Evolution?

The word "evolution" is often unconsciously employed in two different senses. First, "evolution" refers to the small often genetically hidden variations present within every species and which may be discovered in the course of breeding. Or variations may be caused by mutations and selection, which may then be inherited (microevolution). Second, the same term is applied to the transformation of one species into another higher species due allegedly to the accumulation of mutations. This phenomenon may be best described by the term "transformism" in the same sense that the French use the term "transformisme." Obviously the first type of evolution (microevolution) does actually regularly take place. It is a fact and can be observed daily in breeding experiments in plants, animals —and even in man when he is geographically segregated. Breeding experiments with cows and dogs, as well as with wheat and rice strains, prove that this type of evolution or microevolution is an undoubted scientifically and experimentally demonstrable fact.

The transformation of one species into another through mutations and natural selection poses, however, quite a different problem.

Many biologists attempt to confuse the issue by using the factuality of the above type of microevolution as a basis for proving the reality of macroevolution or transformism. For this reason they confuse and intermingle these two quite distinct evolutionary concepts and attempt to blend them into one concept. They use the one term (evolution) for the two concepts and then heap derision on all who deny "evolution" by pointing out that "evolution" (by which they mean microevolution) is a fact.

Boundaries between species are, however, very real biological facts. Microevolution within these boundaries is, therefore, a quite different phenomenon from macroevolution, which supposedly transcends these boundaries between species or "kinds." The first concept (microevolution) requires mere modification of previously existing species conditioned sets of genetic information. The second concept (macroevolution or transformism) requires a qualitative and quantitative increase of a previously existing species conditioned set of genetic information to another set and this by means of chance and selection.

We attribute the existence of Darwin's various finches to microevolution. The minor modifications involved can take place on precisely the same genetic basis as the formation of copulation pads in the midwife toad.[1] If the toad pairs are forced to mate in the water—which is abnormal—the males develop these pads to hold the slippery female when she is wet. The environment acts upon an already existing species conditioned set of genetic information within the toad to produce these pads. In the absence of water, the genetic information for such pads remains latent. The environment merely liberates previously existing genetic information, just as gardening activates my already existing genetic information for calluses on my hands so that my skin becomes tough. Thus microevolution can be induced by minor genetic modifications (mutations) or by the release of already existing latent genetic information activated by the environment. *New information* is not required for processes of this sort.

---

[1] A. Koestler: *The Case of the Midwife Toad.* Hutchinson (London, 1971).

Modified or *newly released* information is sufficient for the phenomenon which we call microevolution.

Transformation of a land mammal into a whale would, however, require the generation of totally new information. The new, highly specific information based on the principles of hydraulics which is required to construct the special teats of a nursing whale mother must somehow be obtained from somewhere. Such information certainly does not arise in mere molecular vibrations, as certain Neodarwinians in their Neodarwinian fervor suggest. Modification of already existing land mammal-teats-information is not sufficent to accomplish this new form of the under water whale teat. Transformation of a species of ape into Homo sapiens would also require totally new information, for an ape does not possess the necessary information to construct the incredibly complex language computer of man. Noam Chomsky's work in this area has clearly demonstrated this fact.[2] Still more new information is required to build the other secondary components of the human language ability (tongue, lips, shape of oral cavity, etc.)

Transformation of one type of finch into another could be explained with the aid of mutations (modifications) and segregation or by the liberation of already existing, but previously hidden, genetic information. Environmental factors and segregation might do just this. But transformation of a land mammal into a whale, of an ape into a human being, or of an amphibian into a reptile requires entirely new, additional information, which is covered neither by mutations nor by the mobilization of latent, already existing genetic information. For this reason, we differentiate between micro- and macroevolution on the basis of how much and what type of information would be required for the hypothetical transformation.

---

[2]N. Chomsky: *Language and Mind.* Harcourt (New York/Chicago/Atlanta, 1972).

Today most leading biologists are of the opinion that mutation and natural selection are the driving force behind both sorts of evolution and that in principle there exists no difference between the two. Many biologists hold, too, that a type of chemical selection served to guide prebiotic chemical evolution up to the primeval cell, i.e. up to archebiopoesis. Prof. W. H. Thorpe, professor of Zoology at Cambridge University in England[3] even goes so far as to claim that mutations followed by natural selection alone suffice to answer not only for the origin of life (chemical evolution leading up to the primeval cell) but also for the various biological species (macroevolution) as well. For this reason Thorpe is convinced that biology can dispense with all further research on the basic principles behind biogenesis and the origin of species. Everything basic has, in his opinion, been fully explained by Neodarwinian thought. Many leading biologists hold similar views and encourage students to accept the same without further investigation. Can we do so, too, without destroying our intellectual honesty?

It is a well known fact that mutations are usually harmful to their host organism. Only a very small percentage of mutations that take place are considered to be favorable to the host. The rare favorable mutation would then be responsible for biological upward development which would thus be due to chance. Increased mutatory activity due to stronger ionizing irradiation should favor evolution as we have already seen. It is so easy to forget the above-mentioned fact that ionizing radiation tends to have an adverse effect on the development and survival of all life. In the struggle for survival those few organisms supporting favorable mutations will find it easier to survive than those without them. The survivors will allegedly produce more offspring than those finding it difficult to survive:

---

[3]W. H. Thorpe. *Evolution and Christian Belief.* Occasional Paper No. 7. British Social Biology Council, Tavistock House South, London (no date given).

consequently the carriers of favorable mutations will, with time, prevail in the genetic pool of their species. As the general rate of mutation increases, so allegedly, will the rate at which favorable mutations appear, also increase. Hence, as we have seen, high rates of mutation should provide high rates of evolution.

If these concepts are valid, the highest biological species should develop automatically and relatively rapidly and inevitably once a primitive primeval cell has been formed. Neither preprogramming nor external guidance of any sort are necessary to this evolutionary concept. The entire evolutionary system proceeds allegedly automatically and autonomously. The scheme is so elementary and apparently logical that few scientists today question it basically and seriously. However, is the situation really so simple and logical as is generally assumed?

Survival of Those Organisms Producing the Greatest Number Of Offspring

Schutzenberger and others[4] have shown the above Neodarwinian approach to biogenesis and the origin of species to be tautological, i.e. meaningless. The reasoning behind Schutzenberger's claim is quite elementary in reality, for he points out that the Neodarwinian hypothesis simply states nothing more than that the organism which survives has survived. Or put otherwise: the organism leaving the greatest number of offspring behind will survive. This type of depth of wisdom is not very difficult to plumb.

Let us pose another question: Is it a fact that those

---

[4]Schutzenberger & Colleagues: *Mathematical Challenges to the Neodarwinian Interpretation of Evolution,* compiled by P.S. Moorhead and M. M. Kaplan. Wistar Institute Symposium Monograph No. 5 (1967), Philadelphia.

organisms reproducing themselves more vigorously than their comrades are necessarily superior, i.e. more "evolved" than those producing less offspring? That this is not necessarily the case, even where human genetics are concerned, is surely perfectly clear. Able, hardworking, intelligent people do not, by a long way, produce the greatest number of offspring. Quite the contrary is the case! In developing countries one of the major problems is that of preventing the reproduction of undesirable elements, as most people know today. Undesirables often reproduce very vigorously, but are often incapable of even providing food for their unrestrictedly large families. Outside the realm of human genetics we find a similar situation. Certainly those plants leaving behind the most progeny are not always more highly developed than others, although they may be ecologically better adapted. Under favorable environmental conditions, rats reproduce very rapidly. With the help of their prolific reproduction they place more highly developed species at a disadvantage, which is certainly not very conducive to the realization of Neodarwinian evolutionary concepts. Primitive moss easily displaces more highly developed grass in a lawn. These facts are so obvious that further specific examples are superfluous. It is evident that prolific reproduction and the production of a greater number of offspring are certainly not equivalent to an upward development and evolution of species, so that we can safely pigeonhole this particular Neodarwinian concept.

Stabilization of Species Boundaries

Some time ago I was working in my garden and digging some borders. As I always make certain that the ground is well treated with manure, I came across large numbers of big, fat, lively earthworms while I was digging. These juicy denizens of well manured soil provided a great source of attraction to all the blackbirds nearby. Healthy, lively earthworms are adapted surprisingly well to their environment within the garden. They flourish by eating their way through the well-fertilized soil and thus aerating it. Of course, they need to react very quickly indeed to the presence of the countless blackbirds and other worm predators, otherwise they would certainly not leave behind any offspring at all.

Now if a mutation takes place within the genes of an earthworm providing it with greater dexterity in its reactions toward blackbirds—let us assume that the worms are better able to hear the approach of blackbirds with the help of this mutation—then carriers of this mutation will certainly fare better in the earthworm's struggle for survival and hence leave behind a larger progeny, for a mutation of this sort increases the worm's efficiency *as a worm*. Whenever a mutation serves to aid the worm in its struggle for survival, this mutation will in principle *improve the worm*—but strictly as a worm.

If, however, an earthworm experiences a mutation which, say, provides it with two rudimentary legs or with a rudimentary eye which not only distinguishes between light and dark, but also projects a real image of the environment onto a retina, then this worm is already ascending the tree of life, it is evolving to a higher species. A worm might even undergo a mutation providing it with a brain or a nervous system in a somewhat superior stage of development (for earthworms). Perhaps it would then be more capable of appreciating the blackbird's song. Yet all such types of mutation producing a more "evolved" type of worm will simultaneously and automatically lead to a *less well adapted worm*. Upward development by mutation leaves us with an organism of *reduced worm efficiency*. Put simply: a worm experiencing a mutation equipping it with a slightly better nervous system or eye might possibly gain pleasure from a bird's song or from a beautiful country view, but these pleasures might actually lower its chances of survival in its struggle as a worm. Thus, if a worm is to survive *as a worm,* then *its mutations must convert it into a better worm*—not into the next higher stage of development within the animal kingdom which will not fit it better for survival as a worm, for at the beginning of the next evolutionary stage, it will automatically be less efficient as a worm.

Natural selection, therefore, does not automatically and inevitably lead to higher species, but rather to the stabilization and improvement of already existing species and species gene sets. It *counteracts* transformism of one species into another and supports the propagation of existing, but better species, that is, of those species in their improved forms. The same concept applies to all plant and all animal species. Those mutations which render the respective organisms more efficient within their own ecological niches are of the most use to plants and animals—that is, those which confirm them in their kind and species. If for any reason any ecological niche has not been already colonized, then a mutation may possibly be able to contribute to its colonization. Darwin's finches provide us with a good example of the conquest of a new ecological niche by the above-mentioned mechanism. But species boundaries are not violated by this change.

Missing Links Incapable of Survival

The above considerations may also be expressed differently. After a mutation has taken place, natural selection will inhibit or oppose transformism in so far as the mutation renders its bearer less adapted to its ecological niche—for the organism will promptly die out. If it is more and better adapted, it will make it a better "worm," better adapted to its niche.

The extreme stability of various species during geological ages points in this direction. Over almost inconceivable periods of times (according to modern biology), bees and other insects have remained substantially unaltered. Coelacanthus (Latimeria) today differs in no decisive points from the old Latimeria fossils. If genetic mutations took place during all geological epochs, we must postulate some sort of dynamic, yet stabilizing, biological process to explain the great stability of these species. Surely mutations *alone* would induce a "species-drift" with time which in fact nature does confirm (*cf* development of the Foraminifera species) in certain sectors. How then can we explain the remarkable species constancy among bees and many other species? We suggest mutation and natural selection as explanations of these constant species boundaries. Mutations are responsible for certain variations within species boundaries. We can explain the colonization of new ecological sectors by Darwin's finches by such mechanisms. However natural selection also acts as a stabilizer within a constant ecological niche. A mechanism of this sort would directly inhibit the transformation of one species into another, for chance cannot provide the information necessary to build legs onto a fish, thus permitting it to leave the water and to walk on land. As we have already seen, however, mere chance is not capable of producing any *new* teleonomic information of this sort.

These thoughts are confirmed by other observations. Paleontology, for example, knows of no missing links between whale species and land mammals. No viable transition form between whales and land mammals has ever been established. Intermediate links of this sort would probably have been incapable of living. But Neodarwinian thought requires the existence of such links: For over 120 years geology has been searching for them in vain.

Again we know of no intermediate stages between the invertebrate octopus and squid types and the genuine vertebrates. Why? According to the assumptions of Darwin and his pupils, early paleontology should have found missing links of this sort in great abundance. Kerkut shows that the entire concept of the transformism theory is scientifically and experimentally untenable.[5] According to Kerkut, existing geological-paleontological evidence provides us with significantly more evidence for a polyphylogenetic origin of life than for a monophylogenetic biogenesis. Nevertheless, modern biological science almost unanimously assumes that all life developed

---

[5]G. A. Kerkut: *Implications of Evolution*. Pergamon Press, Oxford. Second edition, 1978.

from one primeval cell (monophylogenetically, that is). Kerkut cites several pieces of evidence in favor of a separate origin of the various phyla, i.e., supporting the view that they are not all derived from one primeval cell by transformism as postulated by Darwin and his disciples.

If all biological phyla originated separately while displaying the identical genetic language and genetic code, then one deduction and one conclusion can hardly be avoided: the common code and the common genetic language of all phyla can hardly be the result of chance, for chance has never developed one single code. It would certainly not develop any single code thousands of times in identical form by chance. A code always depends on conventions. Chance does not produce any *conventions* at all. *Thus we must deduce that the genetic code and genetic language common to all forms of life must stem from the only source capable of developing any code and language, namely teleonomy or logos.* According to our experimental experience only an intelligent source is capable of meeting just these requirements, for only intelligence is in a position to develop information, instructions, codes, languages, and code-conventions. *The fact that only one single genetic language exists indicates that one single intelligent source must have been responsible for the single genetic code of all polyphylogenetic biology.* There is no other solution to the problem of the origin of the genetic code.

If the phyla originated separately, one would hardly expect them to merge into one another at a later stage in evolution. All experimental evidence available to us supports the proposition that mutations can only affect alterations within the species boundaries and not across them. Experimentally it is difficult to cross these species boundaries without completely exterminating the organism. Yet according to Neodarwinian concepts, the problem of crossing species boundaries should be a simple one, for all biological species known to us today are supposed to have been developed in just this manner (by transformism). Thus crossing the species boundaries should be relatively easy if the Neodarwinian theory is valid.

From the above thoughts we conclude that transformism through mutation and ensuing natural selection is after all not as self-evident and simple as generally assumed today. Experiments prove that species boundaries are exceedingly stable. We must consider, too, the fact that the mutation-induced genetic variations themselves act to stabilize a species within its boundaries. They do not promote evolution in the sense of transformism; on the contrary, they will conteract it.

A Few Consequences

As Kerkut has shown, Neodarwinian thought teaches seven main postulates.[6] Not one of these seven theses can be proved or even tested experimentally. If they are not supported by experimental evidence, the whole theory can scarcely be considered to be a *scientific* one. If the seven main postulates of Neodarwinism are experimentally untestable, then Neodarwinism must be considered to be a philosophy rather than a science, for science is concerned solely with experimentally testable evidence.[6a]

A Variant View: Machine and Concept

Archebiopoesis and the origin of biological species can be considered from quite a different point of view. All biological organisms (plants, animals, bacteria, viruses, etc.) can be regarded as metabolic machines conceived to extract their energy requirements from the environment. Green plants derive their energy from sunlight which reduces carbon dioxide to carbohydrates which are then oxidized to release energy. Animals obtain their energy by the oxidation of plant material. Thus both animals and plants possess the nature of genuine metabolic machines. We must therefore now define the term "machine."

---

[6] *cf* Appendix.

[6a] *cf* Karl Popper, *Unended Quest,* Fontana/Collins, Glasgow, UK 1976.

A machine is an aggregate of matter possessing a project, that is possessing teleonomy. In order to achieve a project, matter must be preprogrammed or—in the words of Jacques Monod—teleonomically organized so as to become a machine. All machines are teleonomically preprogrammed, otherwise they would be incapable of carrying out projects. Matter, in its primeval unorganized state, is not a machine. That is, it is incapable of executing a project so as to construct a machine. In the case of metabolic machines their preprogramming can be regarded as a chemical concept enabling them to metabolize aggregates of matter in order to liberate energy. Teleonomy is the great distinguishing property of all living organisms and of all types of machines. No biological or other machine exists without the teleonomy of a concept. Similarly we know of no concepts to build machines without life being involved somewhere along the line. Biological life is really basically an aggregate of matter carrying concepts and teleonomy which are not intrinsic to primeval matter. Due to the conceptual order of this aggregate of matter, a metabolic machine arises which functions teleonomically and conceptually so as to extract metabolic energy from its environment. Matter in a nonliving raw state carries no such teleonomic program, concept, or teleonomy which is capable of acting as a metabolic machine extracting energy from its environment to serve its own ends. Matter plus functioning concepts can thus produce machines. Primeval matter without exogenously imposed concepts never acts as a machine. Thus the origin of the first primeval cell machine at archebiopoesis is really simply a question of adding teleonomic concepts to matter. This procedure converts matter into a functioning metabolic machine. Thus a cell is really a super machine functioning on the basis of imposed concepts and projects.

If we enlarge on the above train of thought, we find that the origin of species is really an extension of the same principle. If we can answer the question as to how the primeval cell machine obtained its additional metabolic concepts which are not intrinsic to primeval matter, then we can answer at the same time the second question as to how a higher organism arose. How did the higher teleonomy required for an upward development in the Darwinian sense arise? It also arose by adding exogenous teleonomy to simpler aggregates of matter, that is to simpler machines.

It is an axiom of physics that inorganic matter exhibits no concepts, and no teleonomy. The second law of thermodynamics formulates very precisely this well known, but in some biological circles, neglected or willfully ignored fact. For this reason inorganic matter by itself is never able to produce a teleonomic machine spontaneously. An essential machine component, namely teleonomy or functional concepts, is lacking in primeval inorganic matter. It is simply an affront against experimental methods of scientific thought to postulate the spontaneous production of any machine from inorganic matter by the addition of unrectified energy, but without the imposition of concepts or teleonomy of any sort. According to the second law of thermodynamics inorganic matter conceals no self realizing teleonomic concepts. For this reason inorganic matter by itself spontaneously does not build machines. It is quite obviously an experimental fact that machines and concepts do not develop by themselves out of matter. Matter depends on imposed teleonomy in order to build such. For this reason to assume the spontaneous generation of life machines out of inorganic matter today is an anachronism, regardless of whether this spontaneous generation is postulated to have taken place in modern times or in the distant past at archebiopoesis.

Any scientist accepting materialistic philosophy in the form of Neodarwinian evolutionary theory is in reality accepting no-concept as machine-concept, nonprograms as the source of programs, and nonteleonomy as the source of teleonomy during the construction of a cell and during the development of higher species. Since he cannot find concept or teleonomy within the inorganic world of matter, he is left with only two other options:

1. That of searching for these two factors outside the

dimensions of time, space, and matter. Of course, this path is not acceptable to a materialist, for to him the only dimension which really exists is that of the space-time-continuum. For a materialist our space-time-continuum is the only dimension in which he is entitled to search for the source of the concepts of the machine which we call life. If he thinks materialistically and exhaustively, for him no other reality exists.

2. That of searching for these two factors in their anti-thesis, namely in nonteleonomy (chance). This, of course, is a plain gesture of scientific despair, for, according to this solution, nonteleonomy is expected to generate tele-onomy spontaneously without any trace of causality. Thus the materialist who adopts this "solution" (as most biologists do) is in effect throwing in his scientific sponge.

Chance and Machinery

Some time ago I lectured at the University of Graz on the nature of human behavior—whether man's behavior is socially or genetically controlled. During the course of the discussions, I was informed of the story of a farmer living on his farm near Graz who enthusiastically exer-cised a certain quite remarkable hobby. This good farmer collects all sorts of machine parts, cogwheels, engines, axles, funnels, containers, flywheels, petroleum tanks, and gears. These he assembles as best he can so that the heterogeneous parts fit into one another. The parts come from all sorts of different discarded machines, so that it is often very difficult to discover any relation at all between the various components.

One day this farmer was asked why he built such huge, complex, strange machines out of such mutually irrelevant machine parts. It required a great deal of energy to build such machines which did not carry out any useful work! The farmer replied that he was convinced that some day or other his machines would find some useful purpose after all.

Is our intellectual situation in biology today much bet-ter than that of this good man if we agree with the evolutionists that the far more complex machinery of life developed on a similar basis to that used by our farmer? Furthermore, is an occupation at this intellectual level worthy of being taught and researched at University level? Do we seriously believe that biology's "machines" arose at the concept level exhibited by our farmer's hobby?

Machinery at a Molecular Level

Manfred Eigen[7] and Jacques Monod[8] hold two different opinions on the origin of the machinery of biological life. Monod is convinced that man (and life in general) is the result of a roulette-like game. Within the universe man's number was drawn one day and as a result man developed spontaneously out of disorder by pure chance. Eigen, however, does not let chance alone act. He wants to see it guided by the laws of nature. In his opinion it is this guidance which leads to the machinery of life. Certainly this second point of view is not as nihilistic as Monod's hypothesis, but it certainly raises the great question as to whether such guidance by the laws of nature can provide teleonomy so as to produce a machine. The second law of thermodynamics denies, of course, just this possibility, for it states categorically that entropy (an entity measuring disorder and lack of concept) constantly increases within matter in a closed system. Eigen, however, requires that the order within a system of matter supplied with energy will increase spontaneously up to life's order.

How do Monod and Eigen attempt to circumvent the difficulties raised by the second law of thermodynamics?

---

[7]M. Eigen and R. Winkler: *Das Spiel.* R. Piper Verlag (Munchen/Zurich, 1975).

[8]J. Monod: *Zufall und Notwendigkeit.* R. Piper Verlag (Munchen, 1971).

Eigen[9] cites Monod: "The second law of thermodynamics formulates a statistical prediction; thus it naturally does not prevent any random macroscopic system from descending the slope of entropy, that is, of somehow going back in time by means of very minor deviations during a very short period of time. It is just these few and transient deviations amongst living organisms that were retained by selection after they had been fixed and reproduced by the replicatory mechanism . . . . "

Thus we are confronted once more with the hypothesis that minor molecular deviations within chemical systems appearing as decreases of entropy can be fixed and replicated by the genetic machine. While it is perfectly correct that such deviations and transient entropy reductions occur spontaneously, it is incorrect to maintain that they can constitute new information and instructions in the *prebiotic* world. Such may modify existing information on genes, but not generate it. Minor deviations from equilibrium within chemical systems certainly result in transient decreased entropy, i.e. increased order of short duration. Chance alone is needed to produce such microdeviations; but to fix and replicate such microdeviations at *biogenesis*—and here we are concerned with biogenesis and not with the origin of species—*a mechanism or a machine* is absolutely essential, a machine which is telenomic and capable of making decisions. This, however, did not exist prebiotically and certainly will never develop by chance. All mechanisms are teleonomic, and teleonomy does not exist within primeval inorganic matter. As we have already seen, mere entropy decreases produce no chemical-teleonomical information—neither pre- nor postbiotically.

A further aspect of this same problem of minor deviations and their fixation by replicatory mechanisms must be considered. If some sort of mechanism does not immediately fix them, they will certainly be rapidly lost on

---

[9]Eigen, *cf* Footnote 7.

return to chemical equilibrium. Let us assume that some mechanism or other in the prebiotic world as postulated by Eigen does fix such minor deviations and thus permanently summates the transient decreased entropy. Eigen and Monod proceed from the hypothesis that the decreased entropy of the minor deviations is equivalent to a true generation of information. Is such fixation of transient molecular deviations in fact storing teleonomic information?

Information theorists know that the answer to this question is categorically negative. It is just at this point that Eigen and Monod come into collision with the facts of information theory. Information certainly cannot be transmitted without the mediation of decreased entropy of some sort, but this decreased entropy is not identical to teleonomic information. To maintain that the wave function bearing the information spoken into a microphone is the information itself is sheer nonsense. Yet both Eigen and Monod work on the assumption that decreased entropy (wave function by analogy in this case) is teleonomic information, which is simply untrue.

Systems of decreased entropy such as for example the dots and dashes of the Morse code do exist as formations of decreased entropies. However, they can so exist without transmitting or containing any information at all. In order to transmit information via the Morse code, the code's decreased entropy system must be subsequently filled with information according to convention. The Morse code formations must be charged with concepts, information, and messages according to previously arranged conventions. A Morse sequence can represent decreased entropy, but it does not necessarily contain *ipso facto* exogenous, superimposed information. Patterns of the Morse code's dots and dashes can be entirely meaningless, that is, devoid of information. Their pattern (= reduction of entropy) is not necessarily meaningful or informative. Information can be "introduced" into the patterns by suitable convention, of course. A child can observe cloud formations in the sky. It sees patterns and formations (decreased entropy). If it likes, the child can additionally introduce meaning and information into the cloud patterns (= decreased entropy)—the child "sees" writing and messages in the cloud formation. Imagination produces the meaning and concepts and introduces them into the cloud patterns (= decreased entropy), which only then begin to act as transmitters of information. With the aid of the child's imagination teleonomy is thus introduced into the cloud's decreased entropy. But without the child's imagination, codes, and conventions, the decreased cloud entropy possesses neither message nor teleonomy.

Thus the production of decreased entropy by means of deviations and their fixation by some mechanism is possible. But we have by no means produced concepts or useful information capable of building machines of any sort in this manner, for information, concepts, and teleonomy are based on decreased entropy, on which superimposed information is transmitted.

Summarizing, we find that any mechanism which can collect thermodynamic deviations is thereby capable of summating reduced entropy. Eigen, Monod, Ilya Prigogine,[10] and their colleagues are perfectly correct on this point. They are wrong, however, in interpreting such summated reduced entropy as the basis of the true information required to construct the genetic code and its information. Therefore the fact remains that the information required for the construction of, say, an eye or a dolphin's sound lens (melon) cannot have been produced from mere molecular deviations. Reduced entropy or increased order are not identical to the *teleonomic* information dealt with by Shannon's and Norbert Wiener's information theory. But without *this* sort of information and its realization no metabolic machine will ever develop—not even a steam roller, let alone a biological machine.

---

[10]I. Prigogine. *Time, Irreversibility, and Structure in the Physicist's Conception of Nature.* Vorträge zum 70. Gebutstag von Paul Dirac. J. Melra & D. Reidel Publisher (Dordrecht/Boston, 1973), p. 561.

Source of Concepts and Ideas

From an experimental point of view, we are familiar with the biological nervous system as a source of ideas, information, teleonomy, and concepts. This applies to animals as well as to human beings. Every biological organism is a concept executed in matter and distinguishes itself from the inorganic matter of which it consists by just this conceptual, hierarchical characteristic. The nervous system develops new concepts, the matter of which it consists does not. The biological brain develops ideas and concepts and encodes them in symbolic language forms. Among animals similar processes take place resulting in birds' nests, rabbit burrows, spider webs, etc. Man himself can realize his ideas and concepts in matter itself (e.g., the work of a sculptor) or in abstract form, that is, in language, written, or spoken.

In both cases, in man and in animals, the brain executes the organism's new concepts and internal teleonomy. Even if a computer develops new, independent ideas (which is quite possible today) it still simply remains an extension of the human brain which wires and programs it to develop ideas. Thus human brains and their products (computers) create new concrete and abstract teleonomy. All biological organisms represent concrete teleonomy, but the human brain shows superior teleonomy in that it is additionally preprogrammed for the development and use of teleonomic language (logos) for the purpose of transmitting its own teleonomy, which gives man a vast advantage over any animal and its teleonomy.

Life represents a depot, as well as a source of concepts and ideas. The brain is an example, for it is a concept which develops new concepts. This fact can be useful to us in helping us toward a solution of the genesis of biological teleonomy. It is clear that neither man's nor animals' brains were the source of the concepts of biogenesis, for the transparent reason that neither of them were present at biogenesis! The concepts of the brain and of life must have existed prior to the material forms of both, *as is the case with all machine generation.* Concept always exists prior to any machine and no machine ever existed prior to its concept. *Thus we are left with the problem of a preexistent concept being imposed on conceptless primeval matter to produce a teleonomic machine. The following may contribute toward a better understanding of this problem.*

Roger W. Sperry is Hixon Professor of Psychobiology at the California Institute of Technology.   He is a specialist on the functions of the cerebral hemispheres. Several years ago he believed the phenomenon of consciousness to be simply a functional, endogenous, and operative activity of brain matter.   Thus thoughts, concepts, consciousness and ideas would be regarded as simply the products of the brain's wiring.   After many years of research Professor Sperry came in 1965 to a new conclusion regarding the relation between brain metabolism and the mind. He now apparently believes that consciousness, ideas, thoughts, and concepts originate partly within the brain itself, and partly from exogenous sources. In other words, the phenomena of brain activity are partly of endogenous and partly of exogenous origin. Thus the brain can develop concepts within itself, but it can also receive them from "outside."   Hence the brain produces and receives the phenomenon which we call consciousness.[11]

The reasons behind Sperry's changed opinions are interesting.   They result partly from work which he himself carried out and partly from the research carried out on the human brain by Wilder Penfield.[12]   Wilder Penfield stimulated the brains of over one thousand epileptic patients electrically.   He discovered that stimulation of

---

[11]Virginia McIntire. An Interview with Roger Sperry. *Science of Mind* 48 (12), 18-25.

[12]Wilder Penfield: *The Mystery of the Mind.* Princeton University Press (Princeton, 1975). *cf* Article by Robert W. Bass, in *Creation Research Society Quarterly* 13 (1976) 69-70.

certain areas in the brain's temporal lobe produced flash backs which manifested themselves as dream-like pictures from the patient's past. These pictures seemed to the patient like a film demonstration, but which was perceived only within his mind. The recalling of scenes from the past took place mechanically under electrical stimulation and was repeatable. It simply represents a sort of re-activation of the past and its memories without in any way confusing the consciousness of the patient, who was always aware of the fact that he was not really living in the past but was experiencing a flash back. The patient's *mind* remained unaffected, as it were, by stimulation of the brain. It simply registered the result of this electrical activation of the brain circuitry. The patient's mind or ego continued to live perfectly normally throughout the experiment. It simply perceived the dream-like images presented to it by the stimulated brain.

Up to the time of his experiments on his epileptic patients Wilder Penfield held the opinion that the brain produces the mind—that is, that the mind is simply a shadow of the material brain. If this were the case, the mind or consciousness itself would irreversibly dissolve as soon as the physical brain died. Destruction of the brain would thus also destroy the mind or consciousness.

After his experiments on epileptic patients Penfield came to the conclusion that the mechanical production of flash backs by stimulating brain matter does not really affect the mind at all, for a nonmaterial aspect of the consciousness was not influenced by the electric current. The mind simply acknowledged and perceived the material presented to it by the material brain. So the mechanically or chemicoelectrically stored images released in the brain are perceived and read by a nonmaterial, transcendent ego or consciousness. This ego itself, however, stands above the material stimuli as such. Consciousness thus depends partly on the material brain as well as on a nonmaterial psyche, consciousness, or ego.

Penfield came to the conclusion (as later did Sperry) that the mind stands above the contents of the conscious. *Thus the psyche or ego is as it were the legislative branch of the biological system, whereas the brain mechanics (wiring, etc.) represent the executive office.* Executive and legislative powers, however, are hierarchically strictly divided in their respective functions. The mind can perceive pictures and information, concepts, and ideas when released from their storage within the brain. Yet the material brain is not the only source of concepts and ideas available to the mind. Penfield and Sperry are convinced that the mind can receive extrasensory perception. It can, under special circumstances, communicate with other minds, with their concepts and ideas, and this without the direct medium of material brain and its coupled five senses. It can contact other concept-producers and directly perceive their concepts.

So the mind itself would seem to be nonmaterial. It is probably an immaterial concept that is an entity such as other concepts. It can establish connections with other concepts regardless of whether these are imprinted on matter or not. The modern human mind is a nonmaterial concept hierarchically imprinted on matter during life. At death it irreversibly separates itself from matter, but remains conscious and consists then only of legislative and no longer of executive powers.

Materialistic philosophy determines the manner of thought of modern man to such an extent that he experiences difficulty in conceiving the idea of a nonmaterial concept, although he daily employs such nonmaterial concepts within his own language and within his own use of language. Concepts of this sort are often nonmaterial entities which can exist either independently or imprinted on matter.

In his famous book *The Doors of Perception,*[13] Aldous Huxley presents an opinion related to the above considerations. Although a convinced atheist, Huxley believed in the existence of a Universal Think Tank which, from

---

[13]A. Huxley: *The Doors of Perception.* Harper (New York, 1954).

somewhere outside our space-time continuum, somehow stored or generated all *concepts* manifested within the universe. The concepts lying behind biology (e.g., behind an eagle's eye, behind the human brain, or the sound lens in a dolphin's head) did not develop randomly according to this theory. According to Huxley they must have a source somewhere, and in order to solve this problem, he suggested his famous universal think tank. He then proceeded one step further by proposing that the human brain (or consciousness) is capable of getting into contact with this universal think tank and its concepts (by E.S.P.?). Accordingly, the concepts stored within the human brain can establish contact with the universal think tank and its concept contents.

Huxley regarded the human brain as a connecting link between our space-time-continuum and the universal think tank. He also interpreted it as an organ capable of developing concepts independently. Since this think tank can be conceived of as containing the concepts which founded the universe and generated life, contact with such a multitude of concepts would flood every human mind, thus rendering it useless for the biological struggle for existence here on earth. For this reason Huxley held the opinion that the brain represents a sort of valve which restricts and controls the contact between the human mind and the think tank. Certain psychedelic drugs, such as LSD and Psilocybin, are, according to Huxley, capable of opening up the communication valve between the brain and this source of concept which then in fact floods the brain with a "torrent of concept"—as in certain cognitive LSD trips. In order to avoid such floods and their toxic side-effects, the brain usually functions as a reduction valve, according to Huxley, and dams the flow of concept from the think tank into the mind.

Certainly these ideas are speculations and must be treated critically as such. Conversely, Wilder Penfield's and Sperry's observations are strictly experimental and must, therefore, be taken more seriously. Nevertheless, Huxley apparently saw the problem of biogenesis very clearly as being one of concept generation, that is, in old fashioned language, one of "Logos."[14] Huxley did not commit a fatal error of some of his colleagues, for he did not attempt to attribute the generation of concepts and of teleonomy to their antipodes, that is, to chance and to randomness.

The problem of biogenesis is, then, the problem of the origin of chemical and other concepts, that is, of teleonomy. A problem of this importance will never be solved in a scientific way by claiming that the concept developed spontaneously, that is randomly. Evolutionary theory attempts to attribute the problem of biogenesis and of the origin of species to chance and to natural selection in the struggle for survival. It attributes the generation of teleonomy to random nonteleonomy, which is sheer nonscientific nonsense. Today, it is simply unscientific to claim that the fantastically reduced entropy of the human brain, of the dolphin's sound lens, and of the eye of a fossilized trilobite simply "happened," for experimental experience has shown that such miracles just do not "happen." By attributing such marvels to happenstance, we are simply throwing in the scientific towel. Attributing the production of the well-nigh inconceivable concept of a brain or of an eye to chance is not only scientifically unacceptable—it is simply naive, and, because it amounts to an often religious philosophy, it is superstitious as well. It is a fact of experience that superstitions die hard.

---

[14]As we have seen (p. 87, footnote) Noam Chomsky believes (private communication) that the origin of concept and information is a "last mystery," something, that is, with which the human mind cannot come to terms.

Prospect

Many Neodarwinians today are convinced that Darwin in principle destroyed the idea of God, although he himself believed to the end in a kind of indefinable God = spirit and never was an atheist. He tended rather to pantheism toward the end of his life, for with Darwin's help, God as Creator was replaced by a distant principle working by chance mutation and selection. Therefore, many biologists and other scientists disapprove of religious convictions of any sort among their colleagues, holding such views to be unscientific and, therefore, intellectually regressive. We are provided with a well-known example of this attitude in the books of Nobel Prize laureate Konrad Lorenz.[1]

Erich Fromm[2] writes on this subject: "It is not possible to fully comprehend Lorenz' attitude without being aware of his semi-religious bearing toward Darwinism. His attitude, where this subject is concerned, is not unusual and for this reason merits closer inspection as an important sociopsychological phenomenon of our present culture . . . . When the theory of evolution destroyed the picture of God as the Supreme Creator, our trust in God as the Almighty Father of man also vanished . . . . Some of them proclaimed a new God, evolution, and worshipped Darwin as his prophet . . . . Darwin had unfolded the great truth concerning the origin of man; all human phenomena deserving of economic, religious, moral, or political ap-

---

[1]K. Lorenz: *Das sogenannte Böse.* Deutscher Taschenbuch Verlag (atv) (Munchen, 1974).

[2]E. Fromm: *Anatomie der Menschlichen Destruktivität.* Rowohlt Taschenbuch Verlag (Reinbeck bei Hamburg, 1977).

proach and explanation were to be understood from the viewpoint of evolution. This semi-religious attitude toward Darwinism is also revealed by the expression 'the great designers' which Lorenz applies to selection and mutation . . . . [He] even uses the word in the singular and speaks of the 'great designer,' thus approaching the analogy to God even more closely. Nowhere could this idolatry within Lorenz' thoughts become more apparent than in the last section of his book, *Das sogenannte Böse.*"

Konrad Lorenz is very typical of the average Neodarwinian scientist. But not only scientists reveal the influence of the Darwinian manner of thought. Erich Fromm[3] recognizes the same symptoms among politicians. "The 'religion' of social Darwinism belongs to the most dangerous elements within the thoughts of the last century. It aids the propagation of ruthless national and racial egoism by establishing it as a moral norm. If Hitler believed in anything at all, then it was in the laws of evolution which justified and sanctified his actions and especially his cruelties."

Thus Darwin has quite certainly molded the thought of our political and biological elite. And this mold has been of a dubious quality, for this manner of thought belonging to the biological theory of evolution was adopted and applied to politics and to morals. Thus biologists and scientists set the present trend in politics, religion, and morals. If such become convinced that Darwin was mistaken, then the standards of evolution will no longer be applicable to morals, politics, and religion. *Thus a revolution within the sphere of biology would be followed by an even greater revolution in religion, morals, and politics.* The theoretical scientific considerations of the previous pages are pregnant with even more significant consequences for our morals, religion, and politics.

---

[3]Fromm (*cf* Footnote 2, Chapter 2).

Appendix

The Seven Main Postulates of The Theory of Evolution

In his book, *The Implications of Evolution,*[1] G. A. Kerkut draws up the seven assumptions included in the postulate of evolution. These seven assumptions, some of which are covert and implicit, read as follows:

1. Nonliving matter spontaneously produced living matter at biogenesis.

2. Spontaneous biogenesis according to **1.** only occurred once, so that all present-day life descended from one single primeval cell. This assumption is supposedly supported by the fact that the genetic code is identical in all known forms of life (plants and animal). Only the information riding the code varies from species to species. The identical highly complex code of life is unlikely to have developed by chance at different times under different conditions to produce separate microspheres with identical codes. For this reason it is assumed that this chance biogenesis which supposedly ended in the formation of the genetic code took place once only.

3. The different viruses, bacteria, plants, and animals are all descended from one another—they are all interrelated phylogenetically.

4. Metazoa (multicelled organisms) developed spontaneously, without plan out of protozoa (single-celled organisms) according to the principles of chance mutation and

---

[1]G. A. Kerkut: *Implications of Evolution.*   Pergamon Press (Oxford, 1965), p. 6 (Second edition, 1978).

natural selection.

5. The vertebrates are all phylogenetically interrelated.

6. The vertebrates are phylogentically related to the invertebrates.

7. All vertebrates are phylogenetically interrelated.

Commentary

These seven assumptions form the basis and foundation of the general theory of organic evolution. Not one single assumption out of the above can be proved experimentally. Perhaps some of them might be repeated experimentally. But this would under no circumstances prove that the biogenetic experiment actually took place historically.

The Three Laws of Thermodynamics

The first law of thermodynamics states that energy (= matter) is neither created nor destroyed today. Of course, this law contradicts Sir Fred Hoyle's theory of continual creation of hydrogen atoms (now withdrawn).

The second law teaches that although the grand total of energy within the cosmos remains constant, the amount of energy available to us for useful work is always and constantly decreasing. The term "entropy" is a measure of this energy or order which is no longer available to us and is a basic term in physics. Entropy, a measure of the energy or order no longer available to us, is therefore constantly on the increase.

The third law states that the entropy of a crystal is equal to zero when the temperature of the same approaches absolute zero. That is, maximal order reigns at the minimal temperature (-273 °C).

Commentary

Energy-consuming machines can locally reduce entropy and increase order. But the new order produced is financed at the cost of producing greater general disorder outside the new order. Thus, the total increase in disorder exceeds the local degree of order produced by the machine. Matter by itself (matter under the influence of nondirectional energy) tends toward disorder. Its entropy increases. Only a *machine* financed by energy can locally overcome this general entropy increase.

Symmetry and Pairing of Biological Organs

Within the biological world we encounter a phenomenon which is difficult to explain in terms of Neodarwinian thought. It is often overlooked. We are referring to the problem of the appearance in pairs or other forms of symmetry of biological organs.

Many organs within the body exist in pairs: most higher animals possess two eyes with coordinated function resulting sometimes in stereoscopic vision. Many land animals are equipped with paired lungs, paired kidneys, paired gonads, paired breasts (in males and in females), two legs, two arms, two hands, two feet, two ears, two cerebral lobes, etc. Neodarwinians hold that all these organs were generated by chance and natural selection despite their symmetry—and teleonomy. The Darwinians are entitled, of course, to their beliefs and convictions—for religious freedom exists even within the scientific community. But it must be clear that an acceptable scientific explanation of the existence of paired organs on the basis of chance is very difficult to find. Other forms of symmetry, such as seen in plant leaf and petal forms, are equally difficult to account for on the basis of chance. In this book we have stated the factors which exclude chance as the causality behind the development of teleonomy, and this can be applied to the phenomenon of pairs and chirality.

The origin of a single nonsymmetric teleonomic organ can hardly be attributed to chance. But the *paired* development of such organs by chance presents even far greater difficulties, especially if one is an information theorist. There exists, however, an even more difficult additional phenomenon which is difficult to treat on any chance basis. It is the problem of the mirror image nature of the various paired organs within the body. Both hands and feet are mirror images. The mere paired existence of various organs is difficult to attribute to chance. But the problem of the chance development of paired organs is relatively simple to solve compared with the problem posed by the supposedly random formation of paired organs (or paired mirror image molecules) in *mirror image* relation to one another. Paired and mirror image organs (or molecules) indeed pose formidable theoretical problems to Neodarwinians and are, therefore, seldom specifically treated in text books. All symmetry, especially that of the mirror type in molecules, plants, leaves, flowers, and animals, presents a major problem to chance protagonists. How can the shape of a bee orchid or of a fly orchid be explained on the chance postulate? All markings of this sort, such as that of the eagle's eye pattern on the wings of certain butterflies, are far more easily and logically explained on the postulate of exogenous concept and teleonomy.

Human Brain and Evolution

C. Judson Herrick[2] writes: "Each neuron of the cortex is interwoven into a highly complex maze of the finest nerve fibers, some coming from distant parts. It may be safely assumed that most cortical neurons are directly or indirectly connected with every cortical zone. Herein lies the anatomical basis of the cortical association complexes. These interconnected association fibers constitute an ana-

---

[2]C. Judson Herrick: *Brains of Rats and Man.* University of Chicago Press (Chicago, 1928). Quoted from R. B. Livingston: *Brain Circuitry Relating to Complex Behaviour.* The Neurosciences. A Study Program, hg. G. C. Quarton. T. O. Melnechuk and F. O. Schmitt. Rockefeller Univ. Press (New York, 1967), quoted from E. Fromm: *Anatomie der Menschlichen Destruktivität.* Rowohlt Taschenbuch Verlag (Reinbeck bei Hamburg, 1977), p. 250 ff.

tomical mechanism permitting an enormous number of different functional combinations of cortical neurons during one single association chain. The number of association possibilities greatly exceeds all numerical imagination, even that which struggles to assimilate the astronomical figures used by astronomers in their calculations of the distances of stars from the earth . . . . If one million cortical nerve cells were connected in all possible combinations in groups of only two neurons each, then the number of different interneural connections thus formed would total $10^{2783000}$ (equivalent to 10 followed by 2,783,000 zeros) . . . . From our knowledge of cortical structure, we can conclude that the number of anatomically existing intercellular connections available for the formation of short rows of cortical neurons which are simultaneously stimulated within the visual sphere by an image on the retina, would greatly exceed $10^{2783000}$, the number of theoretically possible combinations for groups of only two." For the sake of comparison, Livingston adds: "One must keep in mind that the total number of atoms within the entire universe amounts to an estimated 10^{66}."

The above facts illustrate the incredible complexity (= reduced entropy) of the human cortex as a teleonomic organ. It must be remembered that the information for the project "human cortex" is totally retained in miniaturized algorithmic language on one egg and one sperm. It must be kept in mind also that each neuronal connection required for the cortex's enormous associative capacity is established in the form of biochemical instructions. The entire human being and the entire cortex are built by means of linguistically and chemically stored genetic instructions. All the instructions for this incredible human construction are written in a language which would require more than 1,000 volumes of our information storage systems (books) of 500 pages of small print each. But all this information is stored biologically in a miniaturized form in the incredibly small space of an egg and a sperm using language reduced to molecular size. It seems that even the breakdown of this entire system during aging is also written down genetically, that is linguistically, in the form of appropriate instructions within the zygote at conception.

Any scientist who holds the view that the teleonomy and information required to build an organ such as the human cortex developed by chance with the aid of the laws of nature is either not familiar with the second law of thermodynamics or he is superstitious, for as a scientist he should know that teleonomy and intelligence are required to build an intelligent electronic computer, because the computer matter does not possess the required teleonomy, and neither do the laws of nature governing the behavior of atoms and inorganic molecules when a biological organism is synthesized.

The associative connections within the various electronic computer circuits will never develop by chance collaborating with the laws of nature governing the matter of which the computer is constructed. They are produced by chance neutralized by extrinsic teleonomy and intelligence, as well as by the intrinsic laws of nature. Why do we not apply this experimental know-how before constructing our scientific theories on biogenesis, on genesis of the cortex, and on evolution? Does materialistic philosophy, the basis of so many scientific hypotheses, forbid just this simple step?

Optical Activity in Biological Macromolecules

During a recent lecture tour of some Scandinavian universities, I was asked to address a group of professors on biogenesis. The group included some professors of biology and biochemistry. I dealt with some of the problems confronting materialistic natural science especially with regard to the genesis of the specific chirality of the basic amino acids and macromolecules constituting the primeval cell, pointing out that for the correct macrostructures to be arrived at, the correct chirality of the building blocks of these structures must be taken care of. Large neuroproteins, for example, needed laevo-amino acid building blocks, whereas the double helix DNA molecule needed dextro-molecules to start with. Otherwise, in both cases racemate macromolecules would be arrived at, which would never fit into the acceptor-receptor systems of living organisms.

One professor (I believe a professor of biology) objected most strongly to my suggestion that pattern recognition was the only method available to assure the correct chirality of life's building blocks and maintained that ordinary chance organic reactions leading to macromolecules would do the job. He maintained that first racemate polymeric products would be synthesized by chance reactions, then as the macromolecule became built up to a really large size, the *structural necessities of double helix construction in the case of the DNA molecule formed by chance would force the random process to choose one optical isomer rather than its antipode in order to arrive at the physical structure of the DNA macromolecule.* That is, structural requirements insisted on, say, the incorporation of dextro building blocks, so that, therefore, dextro building blocks would be chosen in the random synthesis of the molecule.

It was in vain that I pointed out to him that if the particular double helix did indeed require dextro isomers (which it certainly did) to achieve the synthesis and if only racemate were present, then a *random synthesis would not choose the one isomer and reject the other, thus carrying out an optical resolution during a polymerization. The chemically identical nature of the antipode would preclude a choice based on perfect randomness in such a case* and the last part of such a synthesis from racemate building blocks would be just as optically inactive as the first part of the synthesis. No *experiment* had ever shown such a type of optical resolution in polymerization processes of this kind unless optically active building blocks were used in the first place.

I pointed out that even if such a spontaneous optical resolution took place, only the latter end of the molecule would be active, the first part would be racemic which would be totally useless for vital cell processes. Such optical resolutions in random organic reactions are in fact unknown and therefore should form no basis for our particular philosophy conceived of and held merely to bolster up materialistic philosophies of spontaneous archebiopoesis. Curiously enough, the professor concerned was a professing Christian—interested in supporting materialistic Neodarwinian theories of primeval biogenesis which stand in contradiction to the Biblical accounts that he, as a Christian, is supposed to believe! It is clear that if even half a macromolecule became optically active by the processes the professor suggested, this mixed optical activity would be repeated in subsequent replication since one cannot store more information than one has on hand. This information, being partly racemic, would serve no vital life processes.

All this goes to show to what lengths scientists are forced in order to hold to materialistic doctrines of archebiopoesis. They are, in fact, compelled to sacrifice some of their intellectual integrity as experimental scientists to maintain their philosophical beliefs—that is, they have to deny experiment, which is the basis of all true science, in order to hold on to their materialistic views.

The whole question of the generation and amplification of asymmetry in chemical systems was treated at an international symposium on September 24-26, 1973, at Jülich in Western Germany.[3]

The above symposium dealt with the experimental generation of asymmetry in the laboratory and with the chirality of organic molecules derived from meteorites and space research. The publication can be thoroughly recommended to any interested in the scientific understanding of this most important problem which must be solved before any serious attempt can be made to explain the origin of life on a purely chemical basis.

---

[3]*International Symposium on Generation and Amplification of Asymmetry in Chemical Systems,* Sept. 24-26, 1973, Jülich, Western Germany, Editor W. Thiemann, Zentralbibliothek der Kernforschungsanlage, Jülich GmbH, Jülich, BRD.

Among many other important facts, two emerged from the symposium which deserve special mention. The first was that the large helical polymers necessary for information storage and retrieval do not form unless optically pure starting materials (monomers) are used. Shorter polymers result.[4] The second fact concerns attempts to generate optically pure starting materials with the help of circularly polarized light. It turned out that this object was practically speaking unobtainable: "Using a large amount of racemic camphor . . . .camphor of 20% [optical] purity was isolated, which is to our knowledge, the highest optical purity yet obtained using circularly polarized light . . . . We wish to point out something important. It is interesting to note that the optical purity approaches 100% as the amount of material remaining approaches zero. A practically optically pure compound (99.99%) . . . . is obtained at an asymptotic point where absolutely no material remains . . . . "[5] Circularly polarized light, thus, does not appear to be capable of delivering the optically pure amino acids required for archebiopoesis, for purity is, by this means, only reached when no further starting material is left over.

As for the starting materials required for archebiopoesis in other parts of the solar system: "We were looking for prebiotic evolution on the moon, for sugars, aromatic hydrocarbons, alkanes, and porphyrins. I regret to say that we have found nothing except a trace of aromatic hydrocarbons and a small amount of alkanes . . . . In one of our first samples we thought we found porphyrins. For a couple of hours we were excited, but NASA in its supreme wisdom had given us a control sample that had been exposed to rocket exhaust and we found porphyrins in there. So obviously our porphyrins came from the rocket exhaust . . . . For all intents and purposes, we had no

----

[4]*Ibid,* p. 137.

[5]*Ibid,* p. 222-223.

evidence of amino acids in lunar samples.''[6]

If chemical evolution leads up to archebiopoesis, obviously matter on the moon—or indeed anywhere else in the universe where temperatures, etc. are compatible—ought to show it. On the moon this is not the case. The truth is that scientists had expected the moon (and Mars) samples to show just this fact and were very disappointed when no evidence for such chemical evolution showed up.

Some remarks by Vester and Wagener demonstrate how unscientific the search is for optical purity in ordinary nonoptically active chemical systems, as the following quotation shows: **Vester:** ''I wonder what all of you are looking for when you work with crystallizations. Either you know that all the deviations from a 50/50 distribution of enantiomers are due to artifacts like asymmetric impurities or to the typical statistical fluctuations in low-number-series-fluctuations which can be produced or even increased by whatsoever physical or chemical factors —or you really still have the hidden hope to discover that L and D are not only mirror images of each other with identical energy contents and identical scalar quantities, but that they have indeed different quantitative properties due to the existence of parity violation even in electromagnetic interactions (as a consequence of CP-invariance). So what are you really looking for?'' **Wagener:** ''We have the *hidden hope,* indeed.''[7] One is thus hoping for something outside scientific considerations to just turn up to justify the materialistic-philosophical view of archebiopoesis—a sort of scientific Micawberism.

The last matter we need to mention concerning the symposium on asymmetry is one to which we have already alluded—that of the necessity of optically pure starting substances for the construction of the DNA-helix: ''It is interesting that the formation of a polypeptide helix is

---

[6]*Ibid,* p. 137.

[7]*Generation and Amplification of Asymmetry,* p. 247.

bound to the *exclusive* use of either one or the other
isomer. As soon as these contain impurities of the mirror
image, the chain length of a polypeptide drops sharply.
This was shown long ago by Idelson and Blout.[8] On the
other hand, we know that short polypeptides are not able
to form helices (because of the relatively high content of
free end groups), the helical form being favored in longer
chains by cooperative transition. Therefore racemic mixtures lead to short peptides, short peptides don't allow
helix formation, which, in turn, don't allow information
storage, which doesn't allow life."[9]

Thus Eigen's hypothesis that life must have started as a
racemate (Eigen also puts forward the opposite view, that
life could not have started as a racemate—see Eigen's *Das
Spiel*) is simply not to be taken seriously, for helices and
information storage, both absolute necessities for life to
originate, cannot be accommodated by racemates.

For life to have originated, 100% optically pure building
blocks (amino acids, etc.) are a prime necessity, and
"ordinary" chemistry, such as that proposed by Miller and
colleagues, cannot deliver this kind of molecule by any
stretch of the scientifically instructed imagination.

Further work on many aspects of archebiopoesis, together with full references, may be found in K. Dose and
H. Rauchfuss' work entitled, *Chemische Evolution und
der Ursprung lebender Systeme*[10] *(Chemical Evolution
and the Origin of Living Systems)*. The main problems
confronting the postulate of a spontaneous generation of
life from inorganic matter and energy are, of course,

---

[8]M. Idelson and E. R. Blout, *J. Amer. Chem. Soc.,* 80, 2387
(1957).

[9]*Ibid,* p. 32-33.

[10]*Chemische Evolution und der Ursprung Lebender Systeme,*
K. Dose and H. Rachfuss, Wissenschaftliche Verlagsgesell-
schaft MBH., Stuttgart, W. Germany, 1975.

not solved by Dose and Rauchfuss. In fact, on thinking the matter over at length, it would seem that the main problems in accounting for an alleged spontaneous generation of life from inorganic matter and energy lie in the materialistic reductionistic philosophy which made spontaneous generation a necessity.

New Finds in the Paluxy River Bed, Glen Rose, Texas, USA

The dinosaur tracks in the Paluxy River, Glen Rose region of Texas, are well known to geologists and others. R. T. Bird of the Smithsonian Institute investigated them many years ago[11] and described what appeared to be man tracks in the same area. He surmised that the latter could not be genuine since they occurred in the same formations as the dinosaur tracks, which would make man as old as the dinosaurs. Plainly, the Neodarwinian evolution theory could not accept the genuineness of such human artifacts. A number of large saurian tracks were dug out and removed by Bird, the holes of which can still be seen at Glen Rose.

Recently further important finds of a revolutionary nature have been uncovered in the Paluxy River Bed.[12] Professor W. Fields, Dr. Frederick P. Beierle, and others discovered in August, 1978, a new find about 200 m. below the dinosaur tracks at Mack's Farm. At that time the water level of the river was very low indeed because of the dry summer, and due to this fact, a carbonized tree branch had been partly uncovered. It had been laid bare by the erosion of carbon dioxide containing water. This carbonized branch was lying embedded in the chalk—a portion

---

[11]R. T. Bird, *Natural History,* (May, 1939), 96 ff., 261, 302.

[12]Frederick P. Beierle, *Creation Research Society Quarterly,* 16, Sept., 1979, No. 2, 87-88, 131.

had been exposed by erosion. Its diameter was about two inches and its length about seven feet. The fact that the branch had been carbonized to charcoal and not burned to wood ash demonstrated that it had smouldered after falling burning into the chalk slime, and there smouldering in the absence of atmospheric oxygen. Many small spherical bodies surrounded the charcoal showing that bubble formation had occurred in the surrounding slime due to the heat of the smouldering. The various tracks to be seen in this cretaceous formation at Glen Rose must have been formed contemporaneously with the burying of the burning branch—namely while the slime was soft, for the latter will have solidifed but once.

Three samples of charcoal were taken for dating by the C^{14} method. Independent laboratories carried out this work. A date of approximately 12,800 years was found.

The carbonized branch was not a root which had grown into the chalk later after it had solidified and then been carbonized. The bubbles and the lack of oxygen during burning both testify to this conclusion.

It is well nigh impossible to avoid the following conclusions as a result of these findings: (1) The branch fell burning into the chalk slime where it was carbonized under oxygen exclusion. (2) This event happened at the time when the slime was soft and capable of (a) receiving tracks and (b) burying burning branches under the exclusion of oxygen to yield charcoal. (3) The fossilized bubbles testify to the soft nature of the slime and to the presence of boiling water in slime to produce steam. (4) Once the slime (chalk slime) had solidified, it would not have become soft again for a second time without losing the already imprinted tracks, so that the formation of the tracks and the burying of the burning branch occurred contemporaneously. Any saurier and/or man tracks in the chalk will, therefore, have been made at the time the burning branch was engulfed by the chalky slime. The C^{14} dating method has shown that these events occurred approximately 12,800 years before the present.

From these results we conclude that any man or saurier tracks found in the cretaceous formation at Glen Rose were made about 12,800 years ago, and that the generally recognized genuine saurier tracks are in fact of about that C^{14} age. Further, any man tracks in those formations will bear the same age and that, if genuine, man and the sauriers lived contemporaneously. These finds, if confirmed, are, of course, totally fatal to evolutionary theory.

Index

DATE DUE: